9 Good Habits
FOR ALL READERS

Grade 8

Authors

Leslie W. Crawford, Ed.D.
Dean of the John H. Lounsbury
  School of Education
Georgia College & State University

Charles E. Martin, Ph.D.
Associate Professor of Early Childhood
  and Middle Grades Education
Georgia College & State University

Margaret M. Philbin, Ed.D.
Associate Professor of Early Childhood
  and Middle Grades Education
Georgia College & State University

ZB Zaner-Bloser

Special thanks to these educators who participated in the development of these materials.

Bonnie Lynn Fahning (Bloomington Lutheran School, Bloomington, Minnesota)
David Kreiss (Thomas Creighton Elementary School, Philadelphia City School District, Philadelphia, Pennsylvania)
Connie Longville (Schumacher School, Akron City School District, Akron, Ohio)
Dawn Pittman (Davis Elementary School, Camden City School District, Camden, New Jersey)
Kristin Scherman (Thomas Lake Elementary School, Eagan, Minnesota)
Carol Toussant (West Elementary School, Minerva School District, East Rochester, Ohio)
Geraldine Weems (Williams Elementary School, Austin Independent School District, Austin, Texas)

Story Credits

"The Planet That Never Was—Asteroids and Meteors" from National Geographic Picture Atlas of Our Universe, © copyright 1980, 1985, 1991 National Geographic Society. Reproduced by permission of the National Geographic Society, 1145 17th Street, N.W., Washington, D.C. 20036; "A Foolproof Plan" reprinted with permission of Steven Otfinoski as appeared in "Within Reach," by Donald Gallo, Editor. HarperCollins © 1993; "Amanda and the Wounded Birds" by Colby Rodowsky © 1987, from *Visions* by Donald Gallo, Editor. Used by permission of Dell Publishing, a division of Random House, Inc.; "Big Little Jerome," from *The Dandelion Garden and Other Stories* by Budge Wilson, copyright © 1995 by Budge Wilson. Used by permission of Philomel Books, a division of Penguin Putnam Inc.; From *Dan Thuy's New Life In America* by Karen O'Connor. Copyright 1992 by Lerner Publications. Used by permission of the publisher. All rights reserved; "The Acosta Family" from *The Mexican American Family Album* by Dorothy & Thomas Hoobler. Copyright © 1994 by Dorothy & Thomas Hoobler. Used by permission of Oxford University Press, Inc.; *One More Border*. Text copyright © 1998 by William Kaplan. First published in Canada by Groundwood Books/Douglas & McIntyre. Reprinted by permission of the publisher.

Editorial Development, Photo Research, and Art Buying: Brown Publishing Network

Photo Credits

Cover photography, title page: George C. Anderson; Models: Nancy Sheehan
p7, Al Bello, Allsport; p9, The Mooks, Image Bank; p11 (left), Nathan Billow, Allsport; (right), Brent Bear, Corbis; p12, Tony Arruga, Corbis; p13, Dave Black, Allsport; p14, Micheal Pole, Corbis; pp15, 21 (top), Corbis-Bettmann; p16, David J. Sams, Stock, Boston; p19, Michael Leyton, Duomo; p21 (bottom), Marc Romanelli, Image Bank; p22, Wally McNamee, Corbis; pp23, 24 (top), Corbis; p 24 (bottom), Chris Trotman, Duomo; pp25, 26, Paul J. Sutton, Duomo; p29, Rick Rickman, Duomo; p30, Greg Flume, Duomo; p31, Corbis; p32, Jonathan Daniel, Allsport; p33, Michael Layton, Duomo; p34, Scott Halleron, Allsport; pp37, 49, Pekha Parvianeh, PR, Inc.; p39, Jerry Schad, PR, Inc.; (inset), Julian Baum, PR, Inc.; p41 (inset), Mehau Kuly, PR, Inc.; (inset), Ken Edward, PR, Inc.; pp42, 44, NASA; p43, Edinburgh, Royal Observatory, PR, Inc.; p45, PR, Inc.; p46, Frank Zullo, PR, Inc.; p51 (left), North Wind Picture Archives, (right), Stock Montage; p52, Fred Espenak, PR, Inc.; p53, The Observatories of the Carnegie Institute of Washington; p54, Space Telescope, Science Institute, PR, Inc.; p55, Larry Malvehill, PR, Inc.; p56, John Sanford, PR, Inc.; p59, Larry Landolfi, PR, Inc.; p60, A.S.P., PR, Inc.; p63, Jonathan Blair, Woodfin Camp; p64, Jay Steven, PR, Inc.; p65, Jerry Lodriguss, PR, Inc.; p67, Corbis Images; p97, Ted Horowitz, Stock Market; pp99, 109, 111, 112, The Granger Coll, NY; p103 (top), Ken Edward, Science Source, PR, Inc.; (bottom), Phototake, Microworks; p104 (top), Lee D. Simon, Science Source, PR, Inc.; (bottom), Corbis-Bettmann; p105, Manfred Kage, Peter Arnold, Inc; p106, Peter Arnold, Inc; p113, Scott Camozine, Science Source, PR, Inc.; p114 (top), The Bergman Coll; (bottom), Peter Arnold, Inc; p115 (middle), Skip Moody, Dembinsky Photo Assoc.; (bottom), John Gerlack, Dembinsky Photo Assoc.; p116, Rod Planck, Dembinsky Photo Assoc.; p119, The Bergman Coll; p120, Cordelia Molloy, SPL, PR, Inc.; p122, George Chan, PR, Inc.; p123, Figure first appeared on p25 as figure 5a in "Pharmaceutical News, Rhinoviruses and Their ICAM Receptors" by Jordi Bella & Michael G. Rossmann, Vol. 5, No. 6, 1998, pp22-27, © 1998 OPA (Overseas Publishers Assn) N.V. Reproduced with permission of Gordon and Breach Publishers. Image provided by The Bergman Coll; p124, Volker Steger, Peter Arnold, Inc.; p127, Fritz Polking, Peter Arnold, Inc.; p129, Liaison Agency; (inset), LeToquin, M. Viard, Explorer, PR, Inc.; p131, Fred Whitehead, Animals, Animals; p132, Mark Newan, Tom Stack & Assoc; p134, Chip & Jill Isenhart, Tom Stack & Assocs; p135, Chase Swift, Corbis; p136 (top), Erwin & Peggy Baner, Animals, Animals; (bottom), Phil Degginger, Earth Scenes, Animals, Animals; p137 (top), John Mitchell, PR, Inc.; (bottom), Wedigo Ferchland, Bruce Coleman; p138, Tom McHugh, PR, Inc.; p141 (top), John Shaw, Bruce Colman; (bottom), Corbis-Bettmann; p143, Francis G. Mayor, Corbis; p144, The Granger Coll, NY; p145, Michael P. Gadomski, PR, Inc.; p146, Perry Conway, Corbis; p147, Wendell Metzen, Bruce Coleman; p148, Raymond Gehman, Corbis; (inset), Tom & Pat Leeson, PR, Inc.; p151, Galen Rowell, Corbis; p152 (top), Ralph Ginsburg, Peter Arnold, Inc; (bottom), The Granger Coll, NY; p153, Corbis-Bettmann; p154, F. J. Alsop, Bruce Coleman; p155, Fred Whitehead, Animals, Animals; p156, Fritz Polking, Bruce Coleman; p157, L. Veisman, Bruce Coleman; p159, Curtis Parker; p191, The Granger Coll, NY; pp193, 195, 198-200, Phillip Roullard; p196, P. Deloche, UNHCR; p197, A. Hollmann, UNHCR; p203 (both), Courtesy Mike Acosta; p205, Arthur Ruiz, The UT Institute of Texan Cultures of San Antonio; pp206–207, The UT Institute of Texan Cultures of San Antonio; p208, 210 (middle & bottom), Robert and Linda Mitchell; p209, © Richard Cummins, The Viesel Coll Inc.; p210 (left), Joe Viesti, Viest Assos, Inc.; p213 (top), Jerzy Tomaskzewski, USHMM Photo Archives; pp213 (bottom), 216, 221 (both), William Kaplan; p214, Courtesy of Yad Vasham/USHMM Photo Archives; p215, Visas for Life Foundation; pp217, 218, 220, Corbis; p223, Detlev von Ravensswaay, PR, Inc.; p225, Stock Montage, Inc.; p227 (left), Baldwin H. Ward, Corbis-Bettmann; (right), The Granger Coll, NY; p229, Spencer Grant, Liaison Agency, Inc.; p230, Eric Pasquier, Saola USA; p231, NASA; p232, T. Raupach, Peter Arnold, Inc; p235, Reuters/HO, Archive Photos; (inset), Reuters, Jeff J. Mitchell, Archive Photos; p237, James King-Holmes, Science Library, PR, Inc.; p238, Shawn Kermani, The Liaison Agency Network; p240, Geoff Tompkinson, SPL, PR, Inc.; p245, North Wind Picture Archives; pp246, 253, NASA; p247, NASA, SPL, PR, Inc.; p248, NASA, Science Source, PR, Inc.; p249, David Hardy, SPL, PR, Inc.; p251, U.S. Geological Survey, NASA; p252, A.S.P., Science Source, PR, Inc.; p255, Tom Bean, DRK Photo; pp257, 266 (bottom), David Muench, Corbis; pp259, 264, Corbis; pp260, 262, William R. Iseminger, Cahokia Mounds State Historic Site; p261, 265, Cahokia Mounds State Historic Site; p263, 266 (inset), Richard A. Cooke, Corbis; pp269, 273 (hook), 274 (top), 275, 276 (top), Jamestown Rediscovery; p271, Corbis-Bettmann; pp272, 273 (bottom), 274 (bottom), Hulton Getty, Liaison Agency, Inc.; p276 (bottom), Tim Wright, Corbis; p279, Luc Novovitch, Gamma Liaison; pp280, 284, The Granger Coll, NY; p281 (top), North Wind Picture Archives; (bottom), Dallas and John Heaton, Corbis; pp282, 285, North Wind Picture Archives; p283, Culver Pictures Inc.

Art Credits

pp35, 61, 62, 101, 102, 113, 116, 120, 121, 125, 232, 239, 241, 250, 252, Fran Jarvis, ANCO; pp69, 71–76, Christiane Kromer; pp79, 81– 86, Richard Walz; pp89–95, Lee, Jared; pp133, 221, 228, James Jarvis, ANCO; pp161, 163–168, John Lund; pp171, 173–180, Gershom Griffith; pp183–189, Stacey Schuett.

ISBN 0-7367-0133-8

Table of Contents

Getting to Know the
9 Good Habits
FOR ALL READERS

A habit is something you do over and over until it becomes automatic. In this book, you will learn nine good habits to use when you read. Read the habits below.

Before I Read

1. Check it out!
2. Think about what I know about the subject.
3. Decide what I need to know.

While I Read

4. Stop and ask, "How does it connect to what I know?"
5. Stop and ask, "Does it make sense?"
6. Stop and ask, "If it doesn't make sense, what can I do?"

After I Read

7. React to what I've read.
8. Check to see what I remember.
9. Use what I've read.

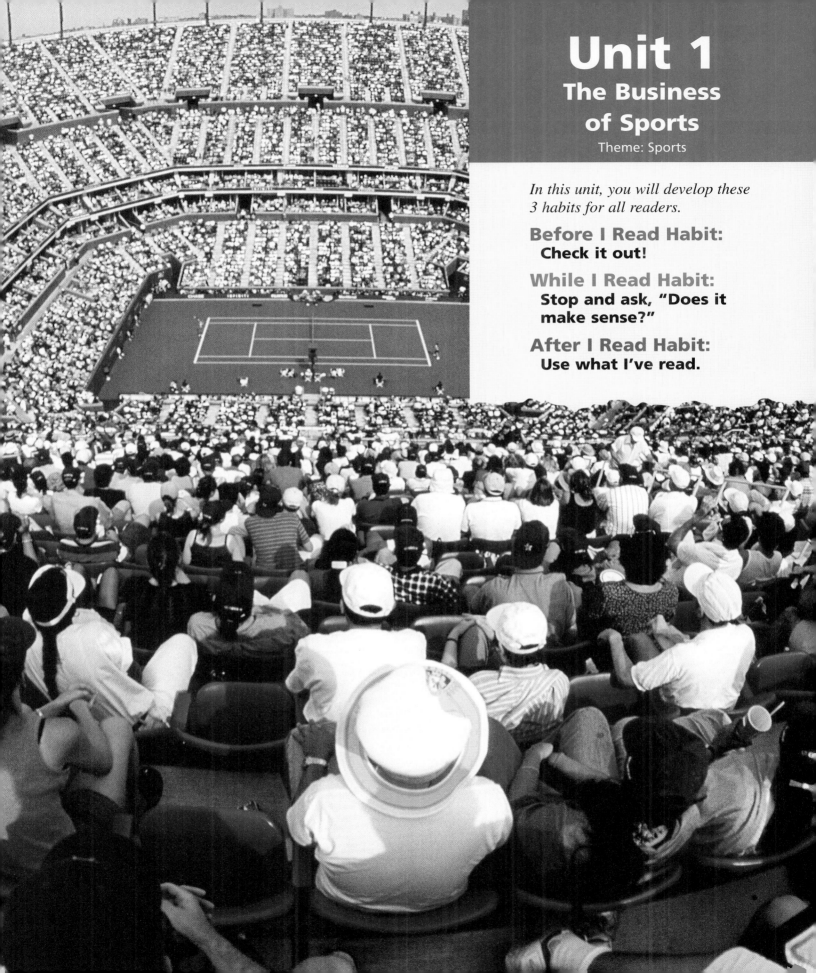

Unit 1
The Business of Sports
Theme: Sports

In this unit, you will develop these 3 habits for all readers.

Before I Read Habit:
Check it out!

While I Read Habit:
Stop and ask, "Does it make sense?"

After I Read Habit:
Use what I've read.

Learn 3 of the 9 Habits

In this unit, you will learn three habits—one for before you read, one for while you are reading, and one for after you finish reading. Start with **Before I Read**. Read the habit and strategy. Then read my notes below.

Before I Read

Which **HABIT** will I learn?
Check it out!
If I develop this habit, I can find out something about what I am going to read so that I know what to expect.

Which **STRATEGY** will I use to learn this habit?
Find the parts that best tell what the selection is about.

My Notes

- Strategy says to find the parts that best tell what the selection is about. Those parts could be the introduction or summary, the heads, the title, or even the first paragraph. Pictures and captions can help, too.

- I'll read the introduction first. Introductions usually tell a lot about an article. This introduction says sports are big business.

- The heads help, too. I see the word "dollars" twice. The title is about the home team.

- I wonder whether the players make all the money. I see something about cities and scoring big bucks.

Cashing In on the Home Team

Introduction

Sports are big business. Every time you cheer for a three-point shot, a home run, or a touchdown, the team owners are cheering, too. But they're not adding up points. They're adding up dollar signs.

These owners have a lot of power and influence over the cities their teams call home. The people who live in the city are proud to have a team to call their own. The city leaders believe sports teams make their cities more attractive to tourists. And business leaders are convinced that sports teams bring in extra money.

So even though everyone knows that team owners make a fortune off their teams, no one seems to mind because we all assume that the cities share in the fame and fortune. Is this true?

Now read the habit and strategy for **While I Read**. When you see ❓, read my notes in the margin.

While I Read

Which **HABIT** will I learn?

Stop and ask, "Does it make sense?"

If I develop this habit, I will stop now and then to make sure I understand what I'm reading.

Which **STRATEGY** will I use to learn this habit?

Jot down personal questions as I read.

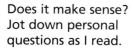

Does it make sense? Jot down personal questions as I read.

The text talks about the money a team brings. Here's a question: How much money does a baseball, basketball, or football team bring into a city?

Cities Score Big Bucks

Some studies suggest that cities benefit from having sports teams. These benefits can be both direct and indirect, but both come down to dollars.

Direct rewards come in the form of rent paid by the team to use the stadium. The city also receives money for the use of luxury suites. And, as any sports fan knows, there are fees for parking, buying a hot dog, or taking the bus to the game. At least part of that money goes directly to the city.

Sports teams also create jobs. When sports teams build a new arena, they provide construction jobs. When the arena is complete they hire a small army of office and service workers to make it run smoothly. All these jobs directly benefit the hometown folk and the local economy.

The indirect benefits can be even bigger. Indirect income includes any money that isn't spent at or around the sports arena, but is still spent because of the sport. For example, a group of devoted fans travels from Green Bay to San Francisco to watch the Packers play the 49ers. These fans arrive in San Francisco, pay for taxis or buses, rent hotel rooms, eat at restaurants, and buy souvenirs. That money, every cent spent by people who wouldn't have come to San Francisco if there weren't a football game, goes into the pockets of San Francisco citizens or to the city.

❓ *Strategy Alert!*

Just how much money can a sport bring to a city? Estimates vary. A 1983 study for the Montreal Expos concluded that the team accounted for $100 million in **revenue**. Around the same time, the city of Denver **estimated** that a major league baseball team would bring $75 million to the local economy. A report in Milwaukee, Wisconsin, suggested that the Brewers baseball team generated $212 million. Over in Philadelphia, which has four major league sports teams, total revenues topped $343 million. And that's just for the city. When the surrounding area was included, the number jumped up to $576 million!

These numbers are just for the regular season. When a city's team makes it to the playoffs, or when a championship is **hosted** in their city, the local economy can explode right through the stadium roof. When Minneapolis hosted the 1987 World Series, analysts figured the city made about $93 million.

Some experts agree that sports fans spend nearly four times as much money as any other type of tourist, with Super Bowl fans topping the list. The Los Angeles convention bureau stated that "there is not a single convention or event that comes into Los Angeles that compares to the Super Bowl." The city of New Orleans hosted the 1986 Super Bowl and found its treasury stuffed with an extra $226 million.

revenue (rev·uh·noo)—income; money earned

estimated (es·tuh·may·tid)—made a close guess

hosted—taking place in

Every game day, thousands of fans with money to spend stream into stadiums like this one in Colorado.

Image Is Everything

image (im·ij)—a general impression of something held by the public

bayou (bie·yoo)— swamp

Many city officials will add another important item to the list of benefits: **image.** A major league sports team can turn a backwater **bayou** into one of the best-known cities in the country. Cities that otherwise would receive little or no attention suddenly get mentioned every day in the news and in conversation. How many people who didn't live in Milwaukee, for instance, would discuss that town if it didn't host a baseball team?

The emphasis on image isn't new. In fact, the first professional baseball team ever created was formed by Cincinnati citizens who wanted to attract attention to their city. In Seattle, a baseball owner once told a reporter, "Tonight, on every single television and radio station in the U.S.A., Seattle will be mentioned because of the Mariners' game, and tomorrow night and the next night and on and on. You'd pay millions in public-relations fees for that."

When television networks broadcast games, they also tend to show footage of the city skyline and monuments. You may never have heard of Jacksonville, Florida, but you can see its best side on television on a Sunday afternoon when the Jaguars are on television. When Jacksonville was chosen by the NFL to host a new team, the mayor announced proudly, "We are now a big-league city."

The public assumes that important organizations only exist in important places. Those places automatically become more attractive, making it easier for tour promoters and business people to attract clients. As one executive put it, "How can I bring people to Pittsburgh to work for Westinghouse if I can't tell them we have a major league community?"

 *Strategy Alert!*

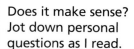

Stop and Ask

Does it make sense? Jot down personal questions as I read.

• • • • • • • • • • •

A team brings lots of benefits to a city. Here's a question I have: Are there any reasons that a city would not want to have a major league team?

Jacksonville, Florida

These faithful fans watch a football game in a blizzard.

It Makes Dollars, But Does It Make Sense?

Cities may become well-known for playing in the big leagues, but major attention comes with major risks. A city can find itself earning a reputation as a loser just as easily as a winner.

The city of Cleveland, Ohio, already had a bad reputation because of its climate. When the local baseball team went on a long losing streak, their failures added to the **impression** that Cleveland was an undesirable place to live. Television audiences saw their visiting teams play in a dingy stadium nicknamed "the mistake by the lake." The city's reputation **plummeted**. Atlanta is another example. During the years when its three big league teams were in the cellar, the local media nicknamed the city "Loserville, U.S.A."

Even when a team is winning, the media attention can be bad for business. Buffalo, New York, has always had a successful football team, but when viewers tune in to games during the winter, they see football played in blizzards and freezing winds. Football fans around the country may admire the Buffalo Bill players, but most fans think of Buffalo as the heart of the Snow Belt.

Even if a sports team helps a city win the image war, the city still runs a risk if the sports team decides to leave. The city then loses whatever status it gained. It may end up being **ridiculed** for letting the team go. When the Colts moved their football team out of Baltimore, one commentator put it bluntly. He said that the move represented "Baltimore's worst fear about itself: it was a second-rate town."

But remember, the main reason cities want sports teams is money. And sports teams equal profit, right?

Well, maybe. ⑦ *Strategy Alert!*

impression
(im·**presh**·uhn)—
an effect on the mind, senses, or feelings

plummeted
(**plum**·i·tid)—fell straight down

ridiculed
(**rid**·uh·kyoold)—made fun of

Stop and Ask ❓

Does it make sense? Jot down personal questions as I read.

• • • • • • • • • •

This makes me wonder: What does "maybe" mean? Do sports teams not equal profit?

Stop and Ask

Does it make sense? Jot down personal questions as I read.

· · · · · · · · · · ·

I don't know what this means. What are "low-wage service jobs"?

Sports teams do bring money into a city. But they also cost a lot. Cities pay operating costs for the arenas and stadiums, police protection, traffic control, and roads leading to the playing site. On top of that, cities almost always give the sports team a tax break, losing millions of tax dollars.

And speaking of millions of dollars . . . when a sports team demands a shiny new stadium to play in, guess who pays for it? The same fan who also spends ten, twenty, or two hundred dollars for a ticket. Cities almost always finance the building of a new sports facility, and that money is gathered through taxes paid by the local population. Not only do fans have to pay for a ticket to get in the door, they have to pay for the door!

Some analysts even argue that the money directly related to a sports team isn't really "new money." Even though reports do note that money is spent on a sporting event, some economists suggest that that money would still be spent in the city in some other way. In other words, if the sports team weren't around, people would still spend money in the city . . . without the major expense of the sports team itself. In Seattle, the chamber of commerce completed a study **confirming** that the Mariners baseball team had brought in $75 to $100 million to the economy in 1984. But they also decided that only $22 million of it would have been lost if the team weren't around.

While sports teams do attract jobs, critics question how much those jobs add to the economy. Aside from construction jobs, which are temporary, most employment generated by professional teams is in low-wage service jobs. ❓ *Strategy Alert!*

A custodian works alone in the empty stands after a game.

Follow the Dollars

So who really benefits from having a sports team?

Some cities may feel they're making a profit, but many experts agree that the real money goes to the owners. When a new facility is built, larger crowds come to the games. That means more drinks and snacks are sold. Although the city gets a tax on these drinks and snacks, the owners usually have deals that bring them most of the profits.

One critic put it bluntly: "I think a question that has to be asked is, in a time of poverty and homelessness and crime and all the other problems this society has, should we be building $400 million stadiums with public funds. In most cases, these stadiums are publicly financed but privately profitable."

But the belief that teams bring fame and money to a city is so strong that cities are usually desperate to keep them around. When the team owner wants something, he only has to threaten to leave. In 1985, St. Louis Cardinals football team owner William Bidwill asked for a $170 million domed stadium. The city offered to build a $117 million outdoor stadium. Talks dragged on for three years, until the city of Phoenix made a better offer. The new "Arizona" Cardinals would play at Arizona State University's stadium. The revenues from skyboxes and high-priced seats would go to the team's owner. In addition, the state of Arizona paid a $10 million franchise fee to the NFL and promised a $5 million practice facility. They agreed to split money from **concessions** and parking with the owner.

William Bidwill

concessions
(kuhn·**sesh**·uhnz)—
stands where
refreshments and
souvenirs are sold

A Place Where Everyone Gets a Piece of the Green

Is it possible for both the city and the team to profit from the relationship? Probably. Most cities want their teams and are happy to have them.

But there is one place where the team and the people benefit. The people of Green Bay, Wisconsin, never have to worry about their football team threatening to move. That's because the people own the team. The Packers are owned by about 1,900 shareholders. Each share is valued at just $25, and owners can't sell their shares—they can only give them to relatives or return them to the Packers.

transcends (tran·**sendz**)—goes beyond

strata (**strat**·uh)—levels

Texans turn out to support the Dallas Cowboys.

When the Packers team makes a profit, the money doesn't go to the owners. The money is used to operate the team and improve the facilities. According to the rules established by the team founder, if the Packers ever were sold, the money would be used to build a war memorial at an American Legion post in the city of Green Bay. And since a top NFL team costs upwards of $150 million dollars, it would be quite a memorial!

But the Packers aren't going to be sold any time soon. Fans seem to truly care about their team, and support them win or lose. Season tickets have been sold out for years, and the waiting list is thousands of names long. ❓ *Strategy Alert!*

Communal Ties

It's clear that financial gain is one of the major driving forces behind a city's desire to acquire successful sports teams. For some, however, there is another, more important, force—the connection among community members. Support for major league home teams draws people together. This in turn can instill a sense of pride in the team and in the city itself. Perhaps a St. Petersburg city official summed it up best when he said, "Sport is one of the few things in life that **transcends** all **strata** of the community. It is one of the few things left in society that ties us together, regardless of race, economic standing or gender." In the end, everyone stands to benefit—those who are behind the business of sport, and those who are at the forefront, supporting the home team.

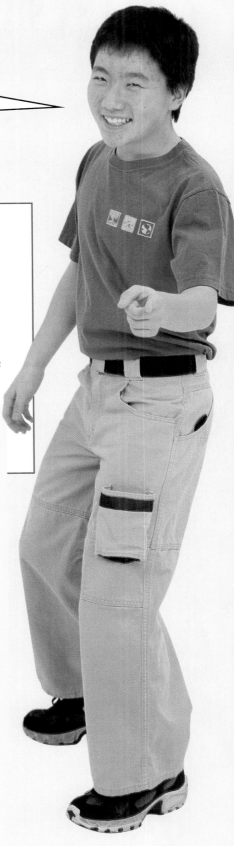

Now read the habit and strategy for **After I Read**. Then read my notes below.

After I Read

Which **HABIT** will I learn?
Use what I've read.
If I develop this habit, I will think about how I can apply what I just read to my schoolwork and my life. This makes reading really useful.

Which **STRATEGY** will I use to learn this habit?
Decide how many of my personal questions were answered as I read.

My Notes

- Strategy says I should decide how many of my own questions were answered.

- I'll look back on the questions I jotted down. My first question was, "How much money does a baseball, basketball, or football team bring into a city?" There were some examples on page 11. The answer was from $75 million to $576 million. I guess the answer to that question varies.

- I'll check to see whether my other questions were answered.

Now it's time to practice the three habits and strategies you learned when you read "Cashing In on the Home Team." Start with **Before I Read**. Look at the box below. It should look familiar! Reread the habit you will practice. Reread the strategy you will use—then do it!

Before I Read

Which **HABIT** will I practice?
Check it out!
If I develop this habit, I can find out something about what I am going to read so that I know what to expect.

Which **STRATEGY** will I use to practice this habit?
Find the parts that best tell what the selection is about.

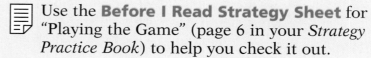 Use the **Before I Read Strategy Sheet** for "Playing the Game" (page 6 in your *Strategy Practice Book*) to help you check it out.

Playing the Game

WNBA player Lisa Leslie aims for the basket.

The ball player steps to the free-throw line. A hush falls on the crowd in the huge arena. The skilled athlete bounces the ball—once, twice—then takes the shot. Swoosh! The hometown fans burst into cheers and shouts. They call out their hero's name: "Li-sa! Li-sa!" Lisa? Yes, Lisa plays for the WNBA: the Women's National Basketball Association.

Formula for Success

In 1999, the WNBA ended its third season. Nearly two million fans went to the season's 192 games. That was the largest crowd ever to attend any women's professional team sport. So far, the WNBA looks like a success.

Reread the habit and strategy below. Look for the *Strategy Alerts!* as you continue to read.

While I Read

Which **HABIT** will I learn?

Stop and ask, "Does it make sense?"

If I develop this habit, I will stop now and then to make sure I understand what I'm reading.

Which **STRATEGY** will I use to learn this habit?

Jot down personal questions as I read.

 Use the **While I Read Strategy Sheet** for "Playing the Game" (page 7 in your *Strategy Practice Book*) as you read.

---

thriving (thriev·ing)— doing very well

The WNBA is just one of the women's pro leagues that have existed over the past century. Some have failed. Others are **thriving**. The success of these leagues rests on one formula. Just as a stool must have three legs to stand, the formula depends on three things: skilled players, eager fans, and money. Take away one of the three "legs," and the stool topples.

A Long History

The image of the fit and skilled female athlete is common today. But that image has been a long time in the making. In the last century, women who wanted to play sports had few choices. Then, two inventions gave them a little more freedom.

In the 1850s, Amelia Bloomer designed loose-fitting pants for women. These "bloomers" could take the place of the heavy skirts and **petticoats** that women wore. At first, the new fashion seemed funny. But women soon found that bloomers gave them a freedom of movement that they had not had earlier.

petticoats (pet·ee·kohts)—a frilly undergarment worn under dresses and skirts

In 1885, the "safety bicycle" was launched. It had two equal-sized wheels. Older bicycles had a huge, wobbly front wheel. This new bike was easier to steer and safer to ride. By the 1890s, 30,000 American women

—in bloomers—owned and rode bicycles. Bloomers helped cycling join tennis, golf, and swimming as approved activities for women.

Exercise was one thing, but team sports were another matter. Team sports involved competition, and competition was not thought to be proper for women. Still, some women did organize teams, mostly at colleges. The first women's baseball team played at Vassar College in New York in 1876. Women first played basketball at Smith College in Massachusetts in 1892.

Bloomers gave women more freedom to play sports.

Title IX

Jump forward in time to 1972. That year marks a turning point in the story of women's sports. In 1972, President Nixon signed a bill called *Title IX*. (*IX* is a Roman numeral and means "nine.") It said that schools had to give girls' sports and boys' sports equal support. Before that, girls often had to be content with cheerleading. After Title IX, girls suddenly had options they had never had. High school girls' soccer and basketball teams were formed. Little League was opened up to girls.

Women were offered athletic scholarships to colleges. More girls began to take part in organized team sports. And interest in joining these teams began to grow. In 1972, fewer than 300,000 high school girls played **interscholastic** sports. By 1995, that number had shot up to 2.4 million. Female athletes finished high school and went on to college. Their dedication to sports grew. Many young women became well-trained, serious athletes. Remember that three-legged stool? The first leg of it— skilled players—was now in place. The next leg—eager fans—got a big boost from the Olympics. ⓘ *Strategy Alert!*

interscholastic (in·tuhr·skuh·**las**·tik)— between schools

Stop and Ask ❓

Does it make sense? Jot down personal questions as I read.

Olympic Gold

Women began taking part in the Olympics in 1900. That year, they were allowed to play in only three sports: **archery,** golf, and tennis. (Notice that none of these are team sports.) The first women's team sport—volleyball—wasn't part of the Olympics for another 68 years!

archery (**ar**·chuhr·ee)— the sport of shooting with a bow and arrow

The U.S. women's hockey team celebrates winning a gold medal at the 1998 Winter Olympic Games.

Following Title IX, the number of team sports for women grew. Women's basketball was added to the 1976 Olympic Games and soccer competition began in 1996. Women's ice hockey was first played at the Games in 1998.

The Olympic Games are watched by millions of television viewers. For many, this was the first time they had seen women playing team sports. American women's teams have won medals in many matches. In 1996 alone, American women won gold medals in basketball, soccer, and softball. The public's interest and excitement for the sports increased.

There are Summer Olympic Games and Winter Olympic Games. Each is played for only two weeks every four years. Fans of women's sports **clamored** for more. Now, two legs of the stool were in place: skilled athletes and eager fans. Advertisers took notice. ❓ *Strategy Alert!*

clamored (**klam**·uhrd)— demanded noisily

Stop and Ask ❓

Does it make sense? Jot down personal questions as I read.

All-American Girls Baseball

The third leg of the stool—money—can make or break women's sports. To understand why, it helps to look back at the All-American Girls Professional Baseball League (AAGPBL). In 1943, during World War II, a wealthy man in Chicago had an idea. His name was Philip K. Wrigley and he owned the Chicago Cubs. The Cubs are a major league baseball team. The war had made a huge dent in such teams. Many players had left baseball to join the armed services. Attendance at games was dropping because fans could no longer see their favorite players. Wrigley thought he could fill this **void** with women players. He also thought he could make some money.

Women playing professional baseball in 1948.

This was not the first time women had played pro baseball. Between 1890 and the late 1920s, there were dozens of women's pro teams. They were known as "Bloomer Girls." These teams toured the country by train, by horse and buggy, and finally by car. At the time, baseball was very popular. Fans wanted to see players on the field. It didn't matter whether they were men or women. Bloomer Girls played men's town teams and some minor-league teams. Once in a while they played other Bloomer Girl teams. This earlier era of women's baseball came to an end with the radio. With radios, major-league games could be heard by millions of listeners across the country. Fewer and fewer people were interested in going to see women's games. The **Depression** of the 1930s wiped out what was left of the Bloomer Girls.

By 1943, Wrigley thought the country was ready for women's baseball again. First and foremost, Wrigley wanted to make money. Wrigley sent out 30 **scouts** across the United States and Canada. They hired the best female baseball players they could find. The AAGPBL started with four teams, based in small Midwest cities. There, they wouldn't have to compete with major-league teams for fans.

To keep the games exciting, the women played a form of softball. The ball was made smaller than a softball to make the action faster. Wrigley called for a longer distance between bases to require more running. Finally, he changed the rules to allow base-stealing. All of these changes were made to make the game more exciting for the fans.

About 200,000 people saw AAGPBL games during its first season. By 1944, there were six teams in the league. Eight teams were playing 110 games in a season by 1946. The teams had names like the Rockford Peaches, the Racine Belles, the Kenosha Comets, and the South Bend Blue Sox. ⑦ *Strategy Alert!*

void (voyd)—emptiness

Depression (di·**presh**·uhn)—time when many businesses shut down and people were out of work

scouts (skowts)— workers sent to find people to hire

Stop and Ask ❓

Does it make sense? Jot down personal questions as I read.

Photos showed the ball players in traditional "female" poses.

publicity
(pu·**blis**·i·tee)—meant to attract attention

chaperones
(**shap**·uh·rohnz)—usually older people who go with a group of young people to make sure they behave

faltered (**fal**·tuhrd)—did less well

The women were not just expected to play baseball. They learned that they were expected to "play the game" in other ways. Wrigley insisted that all the players go to "charm school." There, they learned how to walk, sit, and stand gracefully. The women played baseball in dresses and were told to keep their hair long. **Publicity** photos showed them powdering their noses and putting on lipstick. When the teams traveled, **chaperones** went with them. The chaperones were there to watch the women's behavior. The women were willing to put up with all of this because they loved the game. And the pay was good. The average AAGPBL player made more than $100 each week. At that time, a female factory worker earned only about $40 each week. Baseball was certainly more fun than factory work!

Once again, however, women's baseball **faltered**. When World War II ended, the major leagues were back in action. Given a choice, most fans wanted to watch men's pro teams. By 1954, millions of Americans did not have to go to the ballparks at all. They could watch baseball on TV. When fans stopped buying tickets, business ended for the AAGPBL. The third leg of that "success stool"—money—disappeared. The league folded.

A Tale of Two Leagues

Jump ahead in time to the recent past. The 1990s saw all three legs ready to support the stool. Companies that made sports gear started to make products for women athletes. Advertisers thought that they might be able to make money selling the sports themselves. The spark that made these businesses take notice was the new public interest in women's basketball. In 1996, the U.S. Olympic women's basketball team was hugely success- ful. Their success made heroes of college players such as Rebecca Lobo, Lisa Leslie, and Sheryl Swopes. Media attention was at a peak. ? *Strategy Alert!*

Stop and Ask ?

Does it make sense? Jot down personal questions as I read.

Sheryl Swopes concentrates on her aim.

New York Liberty against Cleveland Rockers

Within months of each other, two women's pro basketball leagues were formed. The first one was the American Basketball League (ABL). This league was begun with money from a group of private **investors**. The first ABL game was played in October 1996. The other league, the WNBA, was backed by the men's National Basketball Association (NBA). From the start, the two women's leagues were **rivals**.

First they competed for players. Members of the 1996 Olympic team were split. Nine of them signed with the ABL. Some of the biggest stars—including Lobo, Swopes, and Leslie—went with the WNBA. Then the leagues competed for TV coverage. The WNBA had more money to spend on publicity because it had the NBA behind it. It spent $15 million the first year. It was also able to get contracts with major TV networks to air its games. The ABL spent one tenth of that amount and made deals with smaller, cable networks.

The two leagues also had different ideas about playing the game. The WNBA wanted to place its teams in the big cities. This is where the most fans were. The ABL chose small cities for its teams. The ABL played in the winter season—the same time as the NBA. The WNBA played in the summer, during the NBA off-season. That way it could use the same arenas for its games. Also, the WNBA could advertise itself during NBA games. They could reach huge numbers of fans that way. Finally, the WNBA had big-name stars. The formula that called for talent, fans, and money came together for only one of the leagues. ❷ *Strategy Alert!*

The ABL quit in the middle of its third season. It had run out of money. Supporters were crushed. They blamed the WNBA for their problems. They criticized it for being run too much like the men's league. The ABL had better players, they said, who were more available to their fans. Their ticket prices were cheaper and more people could afford them. They paid their players fairer salaries. Maybe all these things were true. But even if the ABL was playing better ball, they were being seen by fewer people. Success depends on **sponsors**. Less TV exposure meant fewer sponsors were willing to advertise. In turn, fewer sponsors meant that there would be less TV time. The ABL had the talent and the fans. But it couldn't get the money. The league came to an end in December, 1998. The WNBA survived.

investors (in·**vest**·uhrz)—people who put up money hoping to make a profit

rivals (**rie**·vuhlz)—competitors

Stop and Ask ❓

Does it make sense? Jot down personal questions as I read.

sponsors (**spon**·suhrz)—businesses who agree to pay to advertise during games

What's Ahead for Women's Sports?

What's in store for women's professional sports teams? Several leagues have come and gone in recent decades. These include Ladies Pro Baseball and the Women's Professional Volleyball Association. Still others are coming on the scene. The Women's Pro Softball League recently held a **draft** for its four teams. The National Hockey League is thinking about giving women's pro hockey a try. Soccer officials and sponsors are talking about starting a professional U.S. soccer league. This is due to the excitement caused by the U.S. Women's Soccer Team World Cup win in 1999. The semifinals of that match was the most-watched soccer event ever on ESPN, a cable sports network. The stars of the team—Mia Hamm, Brandi Chastain, and Julie Foudy, among others—have become famous. They now **endorse** sports drinks, clothing, shoes, and hair and beauty products.

The top stars in every sport—men and women— can usually count on product endorsements for extra income. But the salaries paid to the male and female players are far from equal. The U.S. Soccer Federation pays women players less than one third of what men players get. The lowest salary for an NBA player is around $250,000 a year. The women of the WNBA get a minimum of $25,000—one tenth of what the men earn.

 Strategy Alert!

Women's pro team sports have a promising future. Their popularity is not likely to die down any time soon. But the teams will always have to have a three-legged stool to sit on. The athletes may move the ball, but a lot of the power lies in the hands of the fans and the businesses who provide the money. That's how the game is played.

**Brandi Chastain and teammates
celebrate after winning the
Women's Soccer Team World
Cup Finals in 1999.**

Now that you've finished reading, review the **After I Read** habit below. Think about what you read in "Playing the Game" as you practice the strategy.

After I Read

Which **HABIT** will I practice?
Use what I've read.
If I develop this habit, I will think about how I can apply what I just read to my schoolwork and my life. This makes reading really useful.

Which **STRATEGY** will I use to practice this habit?
Decide how many of my personal questions were answered as I read.

Use the **After I Read Strategy Sheet** for "Playing the Game" (page 8 in your *Strategy Practice Book*) to use what you've read.

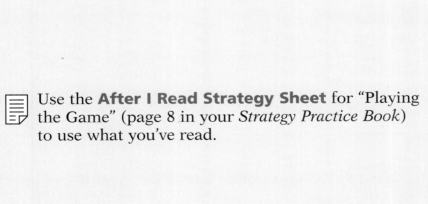

Now read "Majoring in Sports" and apply these three habits and strategies.

Before I Read

Which **HABIT** will I apply?
Check it out!

Which **STRATEGY** will I use to apply this habit?
Find the parts that best tell what the selection is about.

While I Read

Which **HABIT** will I apply?
Stop and ask, "Does it make sense?"

Which **STRATEGY** will I use to apply this habit?
Jot down personal questions as I read.

After I Read

Which **HABIT** will I apply?
Use what I've read.

Which **STRATEGY** will I use to apply this habit?
Decide how many of my personal questions were answered as I read.

 Use the **Self-Assessment Sheet** for "Majoring in Sports" (pages 9–10 in your *Strategy Practice Book*) as you read to see how well you can apply the habits and strategies.

Majoring in Sports

An exciting moment as Notre Dame battles Florida State

Should College Athletes Get Paid to Play?

What's the difference between a college athlete and a professional? Most people will explain three differences. (1) College athletes are students who also play sports, while pros play sports for a living. (2) College athletes compete out of a love for the game, while professionals play for money. (3) College athletics are full of team spirit, while professional sports are a business. That is how we like to think of the differences, but how close are those images to reality?

Are College Sports Big Business?

Read the following description of Team X, an actual basketball team.

Team X went to the playoffs many times in the 1990s. Because it's so popular and well known, television networks broadcast many of its games during the basketball season. The coach is very well known. He earns a million dollar salary and receives several million dollars for wearing a certain brand of athletic shoes when he jogs. Fans spend hundreds of thousands of dollars on tickets and **merchandise** like T-shirts, flags, and other items to wave at Team X games. For this team, reaching the playoffs can mean thousands of dollars in additional revenue.

So what's the real name of this Team X? The Los Angeles Lakers? The Chicago Bulls?

Neither. It's the Duke Blue Devils—a college team.

Duke University, in North Carolina, has one of the most popular basketball programs in the country. No one would question the spirit of its players or its fans. But not many people realize that Duke's basketball team means more than school spirit. Thanks to the skill of its athletes, the school takes in millions of dollars. That, critics say, means it's a business.

The fact is that college sports today are huge money-makers. Millions of dollars are spent to support football and basketball programs. College coaches receive enormous salaries to make sure the programs are strong. Scouts travel around the country to search for the best talent available. Critics of college sports say that this system takes advantage of student players, who get paid nothing. They also say that the joy of sports has been turned into just another way to make a buck.

merchandise
(**mer**·chan·dies)—
anything sold for profit

**Duke University's
Blue Devils**

Athletes or Scholars?

At the heart of the issue are the college players themselves. Some critics argue that the college system should be changed so that college athletes have more time to do what they're supposed to do—study. Some say that these athletes should get paid like anyone else working for a university. Still others argue that the players already do get paid in the form of scholarships given by the university.

What role should college sports have? Should sports be sideline activities while the major focus of college remains study and learning? Or should we forget the idea of education and think of college sports as the career path of professional athletes? It's a complicated issue. The best place to look for an answer may be at the beginning—when the National Collegiate Athletic Association was formed.

Protecting Student Athletes

By the beginning of the 20th century, college sports were already common. Football was a popular game, and different colleges formed teams and began competing against one another. Other college students came to watch "their" team battle on the **gridiron**. Several schools began planning ahead to play each other every year.

As **rivalries** grew, colleges plotted the best way to win. Before there were rules to worry about, colleges brought in "tramp" players. These players sometimes played for more than one school at a time! Students were seriously injured, and even killed, during some of the tougher football games.

In the early 1900s, President Theodore Roosevelt tried to regulate the sport. He created the National Collegiate Athletic Association. The purpose of the NCAA was to manage these leagues, or "conferences," and to protect the students. One of the first rules the NCAA established was that anyone competing in college sports had to be a student who was not getting paid to play. The rules state:

> You (or your family) may not receive any benefit, **inducement** or arrangement such as cash, clothing, cars, improper expenses, transportation, gifts or loans to encourage you to sign a **National Letter of Intent** or attend an NCAA school.

Because colleges prided themselves on being places of higher learning, they were only supposed to admit successful students. This prevented teams from bringing in athletes just to win games, and guaranteed that college athletics remained "pure."

gridiron (**grid**·ie·uhrn)— a football field

rivalries (**rie**·vuhl·reez)— competitions

inducement (in·**doos**·muhnt)—something used to persuade

President Theodore Roosevelt created rules for college athletes in the early 1900s.

National Letter of Intent—an agreement signed by an athlete who promises to attend a specific school

Lowering the Standards

Although good high school students who were also good athletes could be found, they were scarce. Before the NCAA set academic standards in 1986, schools began lowering their academic standards in order to attract bigger and better athletes. If you could make a jump shot or run 40 yards in under five seconds, your grades were less important. It also didn't matter whether you could afford to attend college. Wealthy schools could afford to give good athletes a free ride. Schools **waived** their tuition if athletes couldn't afford to pay for themselves. Technically, universities weren't paying these students anything, so they weren't breaking any rules.

Some critics of these practices say that the standards have dropped too low. The University of Miami once admitted a football player who scored 200 on half of the SAT, a college entrance exam. Two hundred is the score earned by a test-taker by putting his or her name on the paper! It is the lowest possible score. Another high school student, an excellent basketball player, also scored 200. Unbelievably, he was **recruited** by 150 colleges! There is no question that, without their athletic talents, students such as these would never have been admitted to these schools.

In response to stories like these, the NCAA wrote new, tougher laws. These laws stated that, like any other students, athletes had to meet the admission standards of the schools they attended. They required all students to have a certain **grade point average** to participate in sports. As more rules were added, competition for good

Kansas goes for a shot against Michigan State.

waived (wayvd)—didn't ask for

recruited (ri·croo·tid)— invited to attend

grade point average (grayd poynt av·rij)—a student's average based on a point system in which an A equals four points

Former Georgetown University coach John Thompson

students who were also skilled players continued to heat up. Some college scouts secretly offered potential players money and gifts. Other rules stopped college athletes from accepting money from professional sports agents who wanted to represent them. In 1994, seven players on the Florida State University football team were accused of taking money from sports agents. In reality, the agents didn't give them any money. Instead, they took the athletes on a $6,000 shopping spree! When they were caught, four students were suspended and the agents were convicted in court.

Student Athletes . . .

Critics say that the worst thing about the college athletics system is that it fails the athletes. Because some schools put sports first, athletes are not encouraged to focus on their studies. Many of these students leave college after four years with no **degree** and no real education. Critics argue that, in extreme cases, some players may still read at an elementary school level when they graduate college. They are unprepared for college when they start and unprepared for work when they leave.

However, not all college sports programs look the other way. Some coaches insist their athletes meet high academic standards. The Duke Blue Devils have seen 91% of their basketball players graduate since Mike Krzyzewski [shuh·**shef**·skee] became coach. One year when his players' grades slipped, Krzyzewski canceled a planned trip to Australia. The team lost $10,000 in fees it had already paid. But Krzyzewski didn't care—he decided their grades were more important.

John Thompson, former coach of the Georgetown Hoyas, tells his players and their parents that he expects his people to work toward their degrees. He keeps a special seat reserved for one of the most important members of his coaching staff—the team tutor. During his time as coach, Georgetown graduated approximately 98% of its basketball players.

degree (di·**gree**)—title given to a student who has completed college

North Carolina State plays Florida State.

workers' compensation (kom·puhn·**say**·shuhn)— money paid a person who was injured at work

. . . or Athlete Students?

The NCAA has not been able to stop colleges from using players with poor high school records. Some people think that instead of creating more laws, the NCAA should get rid of some existing laws. These people believe that college players are really athlete-students, not student-athletes. That is, they come to college not to get an education, but to play a sport. The education comes second. For this reason, they should be allowed to enter with lower test scores. Also, this side argues, they should be held to a lower grade point standard. Because the school asks so much of them on the playing field, it should ask less of them in the classroom.

These critics also believe that college athletes should get paid to play. The colleges make millions of dollars from ticket sales, television, and merchandise. None of that money would exist without the athletes people pay to watch. So if the university can benefit, why not the athletes?

Some argue that paying the players would have many benefits. If the pay-for-play system were created, the government could apply the same laws that work for any other business. These laws would make sure the athletes were protected. They would even get **workers' compensation** if they were injured.

But those who favor keeping college sports an amateur event reject that idea. They say that it would be impossible to have a fair pay system. Would colleges pay quarterbacks more than place-kickers? Would richer schools be able to pay better wages to get the best high school athletes? Besides, these people say, student athletes already get "paid," partly in the form of a free college education.

Are Big Changes Coming?

There are other solutions to the student-athlete problem. Some of them are simple and common sense, while others mean big changes in our system. Author Rick Telander suggests creating a minor league system for football and basketball. Right now, those two sports get their new players directly from college teams. Almost every single professional basketball and football player plays college ball before joining a pro team. Telander would like to see a farm team system similar to that now used in baseball. He suggests that creating this sort of system would allow young athletes to show their abilities without having to set foot on a college campus.

Another pay-for-play plan includes setting up a trust fund that would pay college athletes on graduation. This would have two advantages. It would give back some of the money athletes bring to the school and encourage them to finish school.

Another, simpler solution was proposed by Coach Krzyzewski. He agrees with those who want to see college athletes compensated. But, he says, that doesn't mean that colleges have to pay their players. He suggests other ways to share the wealth—a free trip home during college break and some insurance, for example.

Everyone seems to agree that college sports programs need some changes. The athletes play in a school setting but are asked to focus on sports. The sports they play bring large profits to the universities, but the athletes see very little reward. Only a few of these college players go on to professional careers. A great many of the rest are left without a solid education. In the long run, which is better for college athletes—money or learning? The answer seems clear, but the debate continues.

How Colleges Make Money From Sports	
Television/Radio	Overall, the NCAA earned $1.7 billion from sports broadcasting contracts in the 1990s.
Merchandise	The sale of NCAA-related merchandise earns about $2.5 billion per year.
Alumni Donations	"Boosters"—former students—continue to support athletics by donating money.
Student Fees	All students pay fees that support athletics at their school.
Ticket Sales	Thousands of students pay to see their teams play each week.
Sponsors	Companies pay large fees to place their banners and billboards in and around college stadiums.
Program Sales	Colleges sell flyers that give team and student information. The NCAA also sells guides that give the year's highlights.
Parking	Fans pay to park at college-owned lots around stadiums.
Concessions	Food and drink provide an easy source of income at university-owned sports arenas.

Put Your Habits to Work in

| Literature | Social Studies | Science | Math |

Before I Read Habit:
Check it out!

Remember to find the parts that best tell what the chapter is about **before** you read a chapter in a math book. Look at the title, heads, examples, and diagrams.

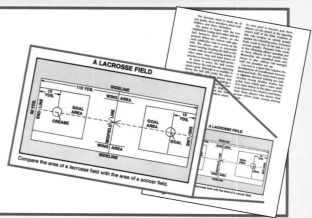

While I Read Habit:
Stop and ask, "Does it make sense?"

Don't read a whole chapter! Stop and ask yourself if it makes sense. One way to find out whether what you're reading makes sense is to jot down personal questions as you read.

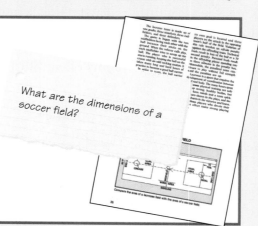

What are the dimensions of a soccer field?

After I Read Habit:
Use what I've read.

When you're reading a math book, you're not finished until you use what you've read. You can do that by deciding how many of your personal questions were answered.

I still don't know the answer to...

You may wish to use the **Put Your Habits to Work Sheet** (page 11 in your *Strategy Practice Book*) to practice these habits in your other reading.

Unit 2
Cosmic Wonders
Theme: Nature

In this unit, you will develop these 3 habits for all readers.

Before I Read Habit:
Decide what I need to know.

While I Read Habit:
Stop and ask, "How does it connect to what I know?"

After I Read Habit:
React to what I've read.

In this unit, you will develop three habits—one for before you read, one for while you are reading, and one for after you finish reading. Start with **Before I Read**. Read the habit and strategy. Then read my notes below.

Before I Read

Which **HABIT** will I learn?

Decide what I need to know.

If I develop this habit, I will have a reason for reading. I will understand it better and remember more of what I read.

Which **STRATEGY** will I use to learn this habit?

Use the title, heads, introduction, summary, and graphics to decide what the author wants me to understand.

My Notes

- Strategy says to look at the titles, heads, introduction, photos, and captions. I don't see a summary in this section, but I see the other stuff.

- Look at the introduction—must be about explosions in our galaxy. I know a little about space, but I don't know what black holes are.

- I see lots of pictures of outer space.

- Now look at the headings. I see stuff about stars and black holes. Maybe the author will explain what black holes are.

BLACK HOLES

The Darkness From Which Nothing Escapes

An artist's version of a large black hole located at the cener of an active galaxy

Introduction

There is a special kind of darkness from which nothing can escape. This darkness is powerful enough to tear spaceships and planets apart. It can grasp and hold light and time forever. It can make matter vanish and cause explosions with a million times more energy than an atomic bomb. Even now, it may be eating away our own galaxy. This darkness has no face, but it has a name. It is a black hole.

Cause for Fear?

While black holes can sound frightening, there really is no cause for alarm. **Astronomers** have calculated that the nearest black hole is hundreds of light years away. This means that even if we could travel at the speed of light (more than 186,000 miles per second!), it would take hundreds of years to get to that black hole.

astronomers (uh·**stron**·uh·muhrz)— scientists who study the universe

Now read the habit and strategy for **While I Read**. When you see ❓, read my notes in the margin.

While I Read

Which **HABIT** will I learn?

Stop and ask, "How does it connect to what I know?"
If I develop this habit, I will think about how what I'm reading fits with what I know. This helps me understand the new material and remember it better.

Which **STRATEGY** will I use to learn this habit?
Jot down a note about what the author is telling me and try to connect it to what I know.

Black holes are not threatening, but they are mysterious. There are many questions about them that not even scientists can answer. For example, no one knows what actually happens inside a black hole. Some astronomers believe that black holes may change or even destroy the natural laws of space and time. Others argue that they conceal gateways to other worlds and other times. Still others think that none of this is true. The mysterious nature of black holes makes them fascinating to study.

What Is a Black Hole?

A black hole is the superdense remains of a dying star many times the size of our sun. When a star this large grows old and burns up all of its fuel, it collapses. Because of its enormous size, it collapses with tremendous force. In fact, this force is so great that the star cannot stop collapsing. It becomes so small and dense, or tightly packed with matter, that it disappears from the universe. The small size and great density of a black hole is what makes it so odd.

This is not the whole story. It does not explain why a star collapses, or why a black hole may be able to trap light and alter time. To better understand what a black hole is, one must first look at how it came to be. The best way to do this is to use a few scientific principles to examine the life of a star.

Atoms: Building Blocks of the Universe

Everything in the universe, from the largest star to the smallest grain of sand, is composed of space and matter. Matter, in turn, is made up of tiny particles called *atoms*. Atoms are much too small to see, but they have been photographed in scientific experiments. Everything we know—animal, vegetable, and mineral—is determined by different combinations of atoms. Because of this, atoms are often termed the building blocks of the universe. *Strategy Alert!*

As small as they are, atoms are made up of even more **minute** particles. These particles are known as *protons*, *neutrons*, and *electrons*. Protons and neutrons are in the nucleus, or core, of many atoms. They are held in place by a powerful nuclear force. Tiny electrons often travel around the protons and neutrons at the center of an atom. Electromagnetic force keeps these electrons in orbit. Nuclear and electromagnetic forces are important because they help matter keep its structure and hold together.

This diagram of atomic structure shows electrons orbiting around a central nucleus. Protons and neutrons are in the nucleus.

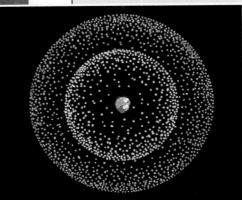

This diagram of a nucleus (four protons, five neutrons) is surrounded by its electron shells.

Stop and Ask ?

How does it connect to what I know? Jot down a note about what the author is telling me and try to connect it to what I know.

The author is telling me about the structure of matter. I know that everything on Earth is made up of atoms. I never thought about matter in outer space.

minute (mie•**noot**)— very, very tiny

This floating spaceman is not affected by Earth's gravity.

orbit (**or**·bit)—route; course

Stop and Ask

How does it connect to what I know? Jot down a note about what the author is telling me and try to connect it to what I know.

The author is telling me about gravity. I know that's the force that keeps us on Earth and the reason that things fall down and not up!

A Force to Remember

Gravitational attraction, or gravity, also plays an important role in holding matter together. All objects exert the pull of gravity upon one another. When these objects are small, like two pennies, the attraction is too small to see. However, when they are very large and dense—like stars and planets—the attraction can be quite strong. Gravity keeps people from falling off our planet and causes a ball tossed into the air to fall back down again. It also keeps the moon in orbit around Earth and Earth in **orbit** around the sun.

The amount of gravitational attraction between two objects is determined by two things. The first is the distance between them. The farther apart they are, the smaller the attraction that pulls the objects together. This is one reason why things in space are weightless. They are far enough away from Earth that Earth's gravity does not pull them down. The mass of two objects also affects the gravitational force between them. Mass is the amount of matter in an object, but it is not the same as weight. A bulldozer may be very heavy on Earth but weigh nothing in space. However, because it is still made up of the same amount of matter wherever it is, it has the same mass both on Earth and in space! ⑦ *Strategy Alert!*

Mass is related to size and density. The larger something is, and the more matter that is stuffed into it, the more massive it will be. Massive objects, like Earth, have powerful gravitational attraction. That is why Earth's gravitational pull on us is so strong.

These are **complex** ideas, but it is important to understand them in order to understand dying stars. It is because of gravity, and the effect it has on atoms, that stars are first born.

How Are Stars Born?

A star begins as a cloud of dust and gas. Most of this gas is an element called *hydrogen*. An element is a type of matter formed by only one kind of atom. An element has a **unique** number of protons, neutrons, and electrons.

Over many millions of years, gravity pulls tiny atoms of hydrogen together. Some of the gas and dust forms a clump in the center of the cloud. As this clump becomes more massive, its gravitational attraction becomes stronger. Material is drawn to it at a faster rate. As gravity keeps drawing particles towards the center of the cloud, the whole thing becomes smaller and more dense.

As the cloud gets denser, atoms of hydrogen begin to collide. The growing gravitational force makes some of them **fuse** together to form a different element, helium. This fusion gives off light and heat energy, and the cloud begins to glow.  *Strategy Alert!*

Fusion of two atoms of hydrogen gives off a small amount of energy. When trillions of atoms of hydrogen fuse, a huge amount of energy is released. As the cloud gets denser, more atoms collide and more fusion occurs. The temperature at the center reaches nearly 27 million degrees. At a certain point, the cloud cannot contain all the energy that is being released.

Then the cloud explodes outward like a powerful nuclear weapon. At the same time, gravity forces it to collapse inward. But it can neither explode nor collapse completely. Instead, a star is born.

complex (kuhm·**pleks**)— complicated; difficult

unique (yoo·**neek**)—like no other

fuse (fyooz)—to melt; to blend together

Stop and Ask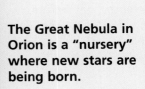

How does it connect to what I know? Jot down a note about what the author is telling me and try to connect it to what I know.

The author is explaining how helium is formed from the fusion of hydrogen atoms. I know that scientists are trying to use fusion to create energy in power plants.

The Great Nebula in Orion is a "nursery" where new stars are being born.

debris (duh·**bree**)—
the remains of something
destroyed

radiates (**ray**·dee·ayts)—
sends out

Now Starring in Our Solar System—The Sun

Scientists believe that, five million years ago, our solar system began in this way. The sun is nothing more than the star the earth orbits. Like all stars, it began as a cloud of gas that first collapsed and then exploded. Scientists believe the planets in our solar system were made from the dust and debris that clustered together after the explosion.

The same forces that built the sun are still working on it. Even now, gravity forces atoms of hydrogen at the center of the sun to fuse into helium. This fusion creates energy that explodes onto the surface of the sun in sunspots. The energy that is released also **radiates** from the sun as light and heat. This is how daylight is produced. Hydrogen fusion is a large part of what makes life on Earth possible.

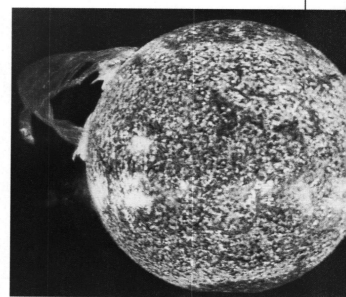

A solar flare leaps from the sun.

But no star, not even the sun, can produce light and heat forever. It will use up more and more of its hydrogen as it ages. Scientists predict that it will take the sun about 5,000,000,000 (five billion) years to run out of fuel. Stars more massive than our sun are hotter, so they will use up their store of hydrogen much faster. Smaller, less massive stars are not as hot. These will take much more time to use up their hydrogen.

Out of Gas?

What happens when a star uses up its hydrogen supply? The answer depends on the star's mass. When a star the size of our sun runs out of hydrogen, it begins to collapse for the second time. Again, gravitational attraction puts a great deal of pressure on the star's core. The helium at its center begins to fuse into much larger carbon atoms. An enormous amount of heat is generated as these atoms grind together.

This time, however, the heat is so intense that the star swells to many times its normal size. The heat is now spread over a much larger area and the star's surface cools to a red glow. When this happens, the star is called a *red giant*. *Strategy Alert!*

Stop and Ask ❓

How does it connect to what I know? Jot down a note about what the author is telling me and try to connect it to what I know.

The author is telling about what happens before stars die. It sounds like how a light bulb burns brighter just before it burns out. That "burn out" is like a little explosion.

A red giant cannot last for long. Its core is so hot that it uses up its helium in a relatively short amount of time. After about 1,000,000,000 (one billion) years, the star begins to collapse once more. This time, there's no more fuel to prevent the collapse from happening.

Dwarves

This is where understanding atoms and how they are built really comes in handy. Remember that protons, neutrons, and electrons are held in place by electromagnetic force and nuclear force. Electromagnetic force, which holds together the outer part of an atom, now meets up with gravity. For a star the size of our sun, this force will end the collapse.

Even after the collapse has ended, the star will remain hot for billions of years. It will also be much smaller and more dense. In fact, it will be so dense that a box, filled with the star's matter and the size of a deck of cards, would weigh about 80 tons! The star has become a *white dwarf*. Eventually, it will cool down and stop producing light and heat. When this happens, it is called a *black dwarf*. ❓ *Strategy Alert!*

Supernovas

Not all stars die in the same way. An old star that is five times more massive than the sun will produce so much heat when it collapses that it will explode. The explosion lasts for a few days and can be as bright as a billion stars put together. A number of elements, such as gold and silver, are created by the explosion and flung into space. This explosion is known as a *supernova*. Even though it explodes outward, the star's core will continue to collapse until it is stopped by electromagnetic force.

Neutron Stars

What happens if a dying star is much more massive than the sun? In that case, the gravitational force may be more powerful than the electromagnetic force. The star will continue to collapse, but now the *nuclear force* that holds the inner part of an atom together confronts the force of gravity. Even if the nuclear force is strong enough, gravity packs the star's particles ever closer together until its atoms

The bright spot on the right is a supernova.

Stop and Ask ❓

How does it connect to what I know? Jot down a note about what the author is telling me and try to connect it to what I know.

• • • • • • • • • • •

The author is telling me that something the size of a pack of cards can weigh 80 tons because it is so dense. I know that some things that look small can weigh a lot! Weights in a gym are small but heavy. I guess that's because they are dense.

diameter
(die·**am**·i·tuhr)—the
distance across

theorize (**thee**·uh·riez)—
to suppose; to think

are crushed. Electrons are driven into protons and neutrons and a *neutron star* is formed.

Neutron stars are incredibly dense. On Earth, a chunk the size of a marble would weigh about a billion tons! Although they were once gigantic, neutron stars are only 10 to 15 miles in **diameter**. Because they are so dense, they are extremely massive. This means that the gravitational pull of a neutron star could tear a person apart. Because the gravity between two objects varies with distance, the pull of a neutron star would rip whatever part of you was closest to it from whatever part was farthest away! The same thing happens to anything that goes near a neutron star.

What if . . .

What if the dying star were so massive that even nuclear force couldn't stop it from collapsing inward? What would stop it this time?

Nothing. Most scientists **theorize** that it would keep on collapsing forever. This means that all the matter that was once packed into a huge star would be crammed into a point too small to see! This point would also be very massive, so its gravitational pull would be so great that nothing, not even light, could escape from it. Perhaps at the center of this point, even time would stand still. This would be a black hole. Which brings us to the question . . . ⑦ *Strategy Alert!*

Do Black Holes Really Exist?

Because they are so small and they trap light, black holes are impossible to see. They can only be found indirectly, by using *binary stars*. Binary stars are stars that orbit around one another. If one of these stars were a black hole, and the other were normal, the black hole's gravitational force would strip gas from the normal star. This movement of gas would be visible. Using this line of reasoning, astronomers think that they have found at least seven black holes. If this is true, then black holes really do exist, but many questions remain unanswered.

The next time you gaze into the darkness of the night sky, don't be deceived by its calm. Reflect on a star's violent birth; imagine its explosive death. If you're brave, think about objects being sucked into black holes, never to be seen again.

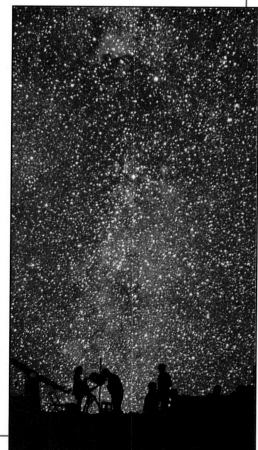

Congratulations! You finished reading. Now read the habit and strategy for **After I Read**. Then read my notes below.

After I Read

Which **HABIT** will I learn?

React to what I've read.

If I develop this habit, I will take time to think about what I've just read. Deciding what I think and what I feel helps me remember it better.

Which **STRATEGY** will I use to learn this habit?

Decide whether the key points make sense and where I can go to check the author's facts.

My Notes

- Strategy says to decide whether the main points make sense.

- I knew something about matter and stars. That information seemed to make sense.

- All the information about how a star collapses on itself makes sense. The article explained fusion pretty well.

- I didn't know anything about black holes before. I can read another article or a book about black holes to see whether the facts match.

- I can check in the library to see if it has a video on black holes, or I could ask my science teacher for help.

Now it's time to practice the three habits and strategies you learned when you read "Black Holes." Start with **Before I Read**. Look at the box below. It should look familiar! Reread the habit you will practice. Reread the strategy you will use—then do it!

Before I Read

Which **HABIT** will I practice?
Decide what I need to know.
If I develop this habit, I will have a reason for reading. I will understand it better and remember more of what I read.

Which **STRATEGY** will I use to practice this habit?
Use the title, heads, introduction, summary, and graphics to decide what the author wants me to understand.

Use the **Before I Read Strategy Sheet** for "Collisions With Comets" (page 12 in your *Strategy Practice Book*) to decide what you need to know.

COLLISIONS WITH COMETS
SCIENCE FICTION OR TRUE DISASTER?

Introduction

Consider a huge object hurling through space at 30 miles a second. Now imagine its impact striking Earth. Trillions of tons of rubble are thrown into the atmosphere and nearly block out the sun. Earth—what is left of it—is thrust into a cold darkness for months. Sound like a scene from a science fiction movie? Think again. According to many astronomers, such an impact could occur if a comet struck our planet. The fiery crash would have crushing effects on all life on Earth.

Reread the habit and strategy below. Look for the *Strategy Alerts!* as you continue to read.

While I Read

Which **HABIT** will I practice?

Stop and ask, "How does it connect to what I know?"
If I develop this habit, I will think about how what I'm reading fits with what I know. This helps me understand the new material and remember it better.

Which **STRATEGY** will I use to practice this habit?

Jot down a note about what the author is telling me and try to connect it to what I know.

Use the **While I Read Strategy Sheet** for "Collisions With Comets" (page 13 in your *Strategy Practice Book*) as you read.

Siberia
(sie·**beer**·ee·uh)—region in northern Asia

meteorite
(**mee**·tee·uh·riet)—a mass of metal or stone that has survived Earth's atmosphere and struck our planet

Stop and Ask

How does it connect to what I know? Jot down a note about what the author is telling me and try to connect it to what I know.

Evidence of Past Impacts

There has been no recent news of a comet colliding with Earth. But evidence does exist that our planet has been struck many times in the past by huge objects. Many scientists think that a comet or asteroid collision caused the extinction of dinosaurs. This happened some 65 million years ago. Scientists believe that an undersea crater off the coast of Mexico is a result of that collision. In 1908, more than 770 square miles of forest in **Siberia** were destroyed by an atmospheric blast. Scientists think that the blast was caused by a **meteorite**. The area still suffers from the impact. Much of the forest never grew back. Evidence of similar collisions can also be seen in the United States. Meteor Crater in Arizona was formed more than 50,000 years ago when an iron meteorite smashed into the desert. While the meteorite was only 100 feet across, it struck with a force equal to 20 million tons of dynamite. It made a hole more than three quarters of a mile wide and 575 feet deep! *Strategy Alert!*

Scientists believe that small objects strike Earth often. So why is so little destruction seen? Scientists think that most of the strikes land in the oceans, which cover more than 70 percent of the planet. Also, craters on land are affected by the movement of wind and water. This erosion often erases all traces of their existence.

Early Theories on Comets

People have been fascinated by comets for centuries. Many cultures believed them to be signs of coming disaster. But ancient people did not fear for their personal danger. Instead they thought comets were signs of future **plagues** or wars. Much fear came from confusion as to what comets were. The Greek philosopher Aristotle wrote that they were **gaseous** objects in the earth's atmosphere. For years, no one could offer a better solution.

Then in the 1500s, the Danish astronomer Tycho Brahe [**tie**·koh brah] studied several comets. He learned that comets live well outside the earth's atmosphere. It was more than a century later that anyone noticed a pattern in comet sightings. In the early 1700s, British scientist Edmond Halley identified one particular comet. He believed that a comet seen in 1682 was the same one astronomers had seen in 1531 and 1607. Halley was able to predict that the comet would reappear in 1758. When it did return as predicted, the comet was named after Halley. Astronomers have since proved that Halley's comet appears about every 77 years. It is possible that people have recorded sightings of this same comet since 240 B.C.!

Strategy Alert!

plagues (playgz)— any things that cause suffering or trouble

gaseous (gas·ee·uhs)— in the form of gas

Stop and Ask (?)

How does it connect to what I know? Jot down a note about what the author is telling me and try to connect it to what I know.

Tycho Brahe

Edmond Halley

nucleus (noo·klee·uhs)—
the center or core of a
thing around which other
things are grouped

spherical
(sfear·i·kuhl)—shaped
like a globe

kilometers
(kil·uh·mee·tuhrs)—
1,000 meters; a little
more than half a mile

The Makeup of a Comet

So what exactly is a comet? Astronomers provide a funny answer. They describe it as a large, dirty snowball. A comet consists mostly of water, ice, and frozen gases mixed with rocky material and dust. Most of the mass of a comet is in its **nucleus**. The nucleus measures between 0.6 to 6 miles in diameter. Around the nucleus is the coma. The coma is a hazy cloud of gas and dust that can be up to 60,000 miles in diameter. Comets have a long, thin tail which also consists of gas and dust. That tail can be as much as 60 million miles long!

Astronomers think that comets were first formed about 4.6 billion years ago. They were created from the same cloud of gas and dust that gave birth to the sun and planets. The outer portions of the cloud became packed into a crowded disk of icy clumps. Over millions of years, these icy clumps took up different orbits. They soon scattered into a huge **spherical** region, called the *Oort Cloud*. According to astronomers, the Oort Cloud is trillions of **kilometers** wide. Objects in the Oort Cloud are so distant that not even the most powerful telescope can see them.

In 1950, Gerard Kuiper [**koy**·per], an American, proposed the existence of a smaller, more densely packed region of comets within the larger Oort Cloud. The Kuiper Belt, as it was called, began just beyond the orbit of the outermost planets. For years there was no evidence that the Kuiper Belt existed.

In this computer-colored photo of Comet West, each color represents a different level of brightness.

Astronomer Edwin Hubble, for whom the Hubble Telescope is named

But observations in the 1990s, including images from the Hubble Space Telescope in 1995, saw dozens of icy objects orbiting beyond Pluto. Astronomers believe that the number of comets visible from Earth is just a small fraction of the many comets in the Oort Cloud and Kuiper Belt. They think that those regions hold several trillion comets. We can only see a few comets. The orbits of these comets have sent them into the inner solar system and into sight of the telescopes. Scientists explain that comets' orbits change when another body, such as a passing star, nudges them into a new orbit. This new orbit takes them into the inner solar system, closer to the sun. ❓ *Strategy Alert!*

Collision With Jupiter

The greatest collision ever seen between a planet and another **celestial** object took place in 1994. At that time, Jupiter was blitzed by pieces of a comet named Comet Shoemaker-Levy 9. According to astronomers, the comet had been in orbit around Jupiter for 60 to 100 years. But then the comet passed too close to Jupiter. The planet's huge gravitational force tore the comet's nucleus apart. Pieces of the nucleus began crashing down. The largest fragments may have been more than two miles in diameter. When they hit the surface of Jupiter they caused gigantic atmospheric blasts. Fiery explosions of gas could be seen as they rose above Jupiter's rim. Because all the impacts were on Jupiter's far side, no telescope was able to see them. But Jupiter **rotates** very quickly—once every 10 hours. Observers on Earth only had to wait 30 minutes after each impact for them to come into view.

Because Jupiter consists mostly of gases, the impacts caused no long-term damage. There were a few dark blotches in Jupiter's atmosphere that remained for several months. Stretched-out streaks could still be seen in the atmosphere in 1995.

Stop and Ask ❓

How does it connect to what I know? Jot down a note about what the author is telling me and try to connect it to what I know.

---

celestial (suh·**les**·chuhl)— having to do with the sky

rotates (**roh**·tayts)— turns or spins on an axis

The dark blue spots in Jupiter's southern hemisphere show where chunks of comet smashed into the atmosphere.

Earth vs. a Comet

How would the earth fare if it were hit by a comet? That depends on its size. A large comet—0.6 miles or more—would hit the earth with an energy equal to a trillion tons of dynamite. Flashing through our atmosphere in about two seconds, it would crash into the ground. The force would be so great that it would explode into an immense fireball. The shock wave from the blast would level every single thing within 60 miles. Beyond that area of total destruction, another 600 miles would suffer extreme damage. The collision would produce a crater at least 12 miles across and several miles deep. The dust and gas would spread around the planet and **obscure** the sun.

Scientists assure us that the earth would most likely survive this impact. But it would probably cause great amounts of damage throughout the planet. Astronomers predict that most of the planet's vegetation would be ruined. Such a loss would have a devastating effect on human and animal life. Whatever managed to survive would sink into a prolonged **dark age**. Even if the comet were to hit the ocean, disaster would result. A mile-high tidal wave would rush toward land at almost 600 miles an hour. *Strategy Alert!*

Fortunately, such collisions with large comets are very rare. Astronomers believe that an object that is 0.6 miles wide strikes the earth only once every million years. Objects that are 6 miles across are likely to strike only once in 100 million years. This prediction is based on **geological** records of impact craters on Earth. Strikes by smaller bodies, such as the one that created Arizona's Meteor Crater, are more frequent. Smaller-scale collisions don't worry scientists as much because destruction would be limited to a relatively small area.

obscure (ob•**skyoor**)—to conceal; to cover; to hide

dark age—a period of time in which there is only darkness

Stop and Ask ?

How does it connect to what I know? Jot down a note about what the author is telling me and try to connect it to what I know.

geological (jee•uh•**loj**•i•kuhl)— having to do with the study of the history and structure of the earth

How Can Our Planet Be Protected?

It is not at all likely that a large comet or **asteroid** will hit the earth anytime soon. In fact, scientists today believe that there is only a one percent chance that in the next 1,000 years the earth will be hit by a large asteroid. Some of the latest research suggests that Earth shares its space in the inner solar system with only about 700 of the 1,000–2,000 asteroids that are out there. So the earth is not at as great a risk of collision as scientists once believed. But several ideas to prevent such a disaster have been suggested. Some astronomers have proposed using a network of telescopes to constantly search the solar system. This system would enable scientists to see all objects that are dangerously close to the earth.

Unfortunately, just seeing a comet heading to Earth does not solve the problem. We need to find a way to stop or lessen the impact. While scientists have some good ideas, they all involve some risk. One idea is to send nuclear-armed rockets into space. These rockets would blow up the comet or guide it into a new orbit. But such a plan would require extremely careful calculations. Trying to destroy the comet could be very dangerous. If it were simply broken into large pieces, those chunks might fall down over a large region of the earth and cause destruction. Changing the course of the object's orbit might be a better plan. That could be done by setting off missiles close to the object which would change its motion but not break it apart. *Strategy Alert!*

asteroid (**as**·tuh·royd)— a small celestial body that orbits the sun, mostly between the orbits of Mars and Jupiter

Stop and Ask ?

How does it connect to what I know? Jot down a note about what the author is telling me and try to connect it to what I know.

Objects in space send waves that cannot be seen. These waves can be detected by special telescopes, such as the radio telescopes shown here.

A better idea is to avoid explosive devices altogether. But plenty of advance warning—several years—would be needed. One plan sends astronauts directly to a threatening comet or asteroid. The astronauts would attach powerful rocket engines on the object to help it find a new, harmless orbit. Another solution suggests that astronauts fit the comet with a huge "solar sail." This sail would capture the pressure of the sunlight. The pressure would work like wind and slowly "sail" the comet away from Earth.

Luckily, we will probably have plenty of time to find the best solution. Astronomers remind us of the long time between impacts. The chance of a large comet striking the earth anytime soon is very slim. And so, while we shouldn't ignore the threat of comets, we can be reasonably sure that the only comets we will be seeing are the ones in the sky.

Summary

The more we learn about comets, the more we realize their immense potential for great destruction. The collision between Jupiter and a celestial object clearly shows the great force with which comets can strike. We have the results of strikes by celestial objects in Arizona and Siberia to remind us of how much damage they can do. All of this information helps us gain an idea of what would happen if a comet were to strike Earth. Scientists and engineers have proposed risky plans to help protect the planet in the case of a comet collision. But more than anything, all our knowledge about comets assures us that there is relatively low risk for any comet strike on Earth anytime soon. *Strategy Alert!*

Stop and Ask

How does it connect to what I know? Jot down a note about what the author is telling me and try to connect it to what I know.

Arizona's Meteor Crater is thought to be more than 50,000 years old.

Now that you've finished reading, review the **After I Read** habit below. Think about what you've read in "Collisions With Comets" as you practice the strategy.

After I Read

Which **HABIT** will I practice?
React to what I've read.
If I develop this habit, I will take time to think about what I've just read. Deciding what I think and what I feel helps me remember it better.

Which **STRATEGY** will I use to practice this habit?
Decide whether the key points make sense and where I can go to check the author's facts.

Use the **After I Read Strategy Sheet** for "Collisions With Comets" (page 14 in your *Strategy Practice Book*) to react to what you've read.

Now read "A Planet That Never Was—Asteroids and Meteors" and apply these habits and strategies.

Before I Read

Which **HABIT** will I apply?
Decide what I need to know.

Which **STRATEGY** will I use to apply this habit?
Use the title, heads, introduction, summary, and graphics to decide what the author wants me to understand.

While I Read

Which **HABIT** will I apply?
Stop and ask, "How does it connect to what I know?"

Which **STRATEGY** will I use to apply this habit?
Jot down a note about what the author is telling me and try to connect it to what I know.

After I Read

Which **HABIT** will I apply?
React to what I've read.

Which **STRATEGY** will I use to apply this habit?
Decide whether the key points make sense and where I can go to check the author's facts.

 Use the **Self-Assessment Sheet** for "A Planet That Never Was—Asteroids and Meteors" (pages 15 and 16 in your *Strategy Practice Book*) as you read to see how well you can apply the habits and strategies.

Like most people, you have probably looked up at the sky on a clear night. You have seen Earth's moon reflecting the light of the sun. You may have found patterns in the billions of glowing specks that are stars and planets. Have you ever wondered what else exists out there? Many smaller objects can also be found in space. Among these are asteroids, meteors, and comets. As you saw in the last selection, these objects pose little threat to Earth, but what else do we know about them? Where did they come from? Why are they there?

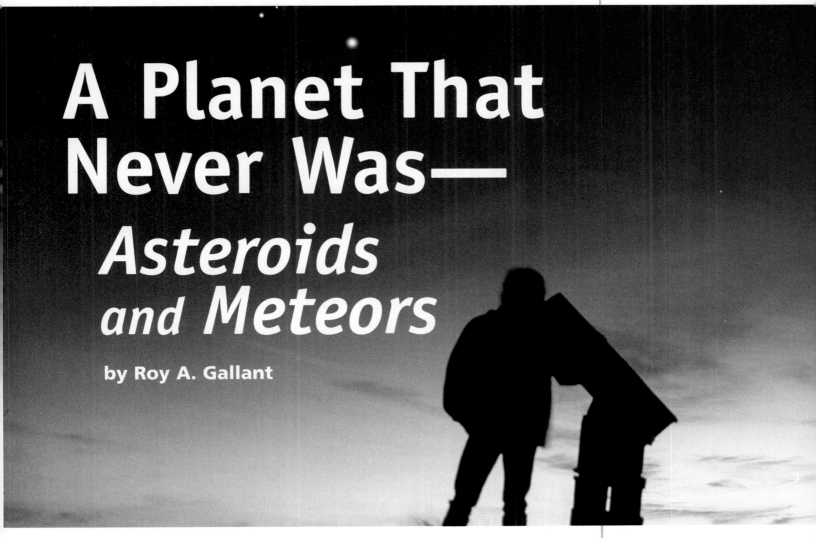

A Planet That Never Was—
Asteroids and Meteors
by Roy A. Gallant

Asteroids and Meteors

Some call them "minor planets." Others have called them "planetoids." They are the asteroids, tens of thousands of tumbling, sometimes bumping lumps of rock-metal fragments that wheel around the sun, most of them in a broad orbit between Mars and Jupiter. About 102 million kilometers beyond the orbit of Mars we come to the inner edge of this belt of asteroids. It stretches on for about 165 million kilometers toward Jupiter's orbit.

The face of Mercury is dotted by many craters.

craters (**kray**·tuhrz)—
holes in the earth caused
by explosions or impacts

Here, as we look toward rosy, banded Jupiter, we can see that there is a lot of space between individual asteroids. Although we have never landed on an asteroid, we have gone close to a few of them. They are pitted with many **craters,** like Mercury or our moon.

During the early ages of our solar system, thousands of these cosmic bombs plunged into Mercury, Venus, Earth, Mars, and Jupiter, as well as into the planets' moons and into each other. And most likely, small pieces of them—the meteoroids—will keep doing so from time to time over the billions of years left in the life of our solar system.

Because the asteroids batter each other, and because they are so small, few of them are neatly **sphere**-shaped.

sphere (sfear)—ball;
globe

There are as many asteroid orbits as there are asteroids. Many of these objects, like Ceres [**seer**·eez], stay within the asteroid belt, a wide band between Mars and Jupiter. A planet ought to be there, astronomers once said; when they found asteroids instead, they thought these might be its pieces. But that's unlikely. All known asteroids lumped together would still be smaller than the moon. Now and then a big one crosses Earth's orbit. Every million years or so, three or four of them ram into Earth and blast out craters many kilometers across.

Small asteroids have irregular shapes and the same composition outside and in—nickel and iron, or stone, or a little of both. Some asteroids may also contain large amounts of carbon, which gives them a dull, blackish color. Asteroids range in size from big Ceres to tiny lumps. On Ceres you would weigh 1/33 your Earth weight—and on a very small asteroid you would weigh so little that you might jump up and never come down.

Oddballs of the solar system, asteroids come in many sizes and shapes. First to be discovered was Ceres, the largest known. Over 3,300 are now numbered; hundreds of thousands more may whirl about, too small to be seen. Phobos [**foh**·bohs], a moon of Mars, may be a captured asteroid. Some asteroids are so massive [that] their own gravitation has molded them into spheres. Collisions may shatter them or join them into odd shapes.

In the late 1700's German astronomers, calling themselves "celestial police," began to search with telescopes for a missing planet. They did this because in 1772 an astronomer, Johann [**yoh**·hahn] Bode, had **publicized** a mathematical law, invented by John Daniel Titius, which gave the relative positions of the planets in the solar system. However, something was **amiss**. In the gap between the orbits of Mars and Jupiter, Bode said there should be a planet.

publicized
(**pub**·li·siezd)—
announced

amiss (uh·**mis**)—
not as it should be

Minor Planets

On January 1, 1801, the Sicilian astronomer Giuseppi Piazzi [juh·**sep**·ee pee·**ahtz**·ee] found something which he thought was the missing planet. Later named Ceres, it turned out to be a mere pebble of a planet about 945 kilometers across—a third the size of the moon. Then in 1802 another small planet, Pallas, was discovered in the gap. It was half the size of Ceres. In 1804 a third such object, Juno, was found—less than half the size of Pallas. Then in 1807 a German astronomer saw a fourth, Vesta— the brightest asteroid and the only one that can be seen with the naked eye. By 1890 astronomers had found 300 of these planets in the Mars-Jupiter gap. Today we know the orbits of more than 5,000. There may be hundreds of thousands. Most are boulder-size to mountain-size lumps of rock and metal that we call *asteroids,* or *minor planets*.

Asteroid Summary		
Name	**Discoverer**	**Date**
Ceres	G. Piazzi	1801
Davida	R. Dugan	1903
Eunomia	A. De Gasparis	1851
Europa	H. Goldschmidt	1858
Gaspra	G. Neujmin	1916
Hygiea	A. De Gasparis	1849
Ida	J. Palisa	1884
Interamnia	V. Cerulli	1910
Juno	C.L. Harding	1804
Pallas	H. Olbers	1802
Psyche	A. De Gasparis	1852
Sylvia	N. Pogson	1866
Vesta	H. Olbers	1807

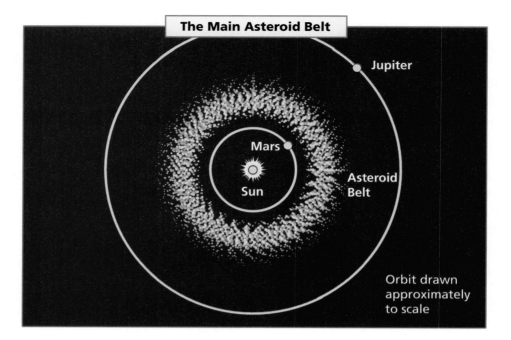

The Main Asteroid Belt

Jupiter

Mars

Sun

Asteroid Belt

Orbit drawn approximately to scale

Earth-Crossers

The average time an asteroid takes to go around its orbit is about five Earth years. A few have long, stretched-out orbits that take them very close to the sun—and to Earth. These are called Apollo Objects, or Earth-crossers, because they swoop in so close and **intersect** the orbit of Earth from time to time. (Their name comes from the asteroid Apollo, the first seen to cross our orbit.) In all, we know of about 40 Apollos. Some astronomers suggest that certain Earth-crossers may be the remains of old comets, while others are asteroids.

Eros hurtles through space, spinning rapidly at the rate of once every 5.27 hours. It has come within 23 million kilometers of Earth. Apollo has come within about four million kilometers of us. And Hermes [**hur**·meez] has zoomed to within 770,000 kilometers, only twice the moon's distance from Earth.

Astronomers don't worry too much when the Earth-crossers sweep in close to us. The chance of one of these cosmic mountains crashing into us is pretty small—a **catastrophic** hit perhaps every 65 to 100 million years. Some experts think the interval may be much shorter. But if a giant should strike, it could produce an explosion as great as 20,000 megaton hydrogen bombs, and might blast out a crater hundreds of meters deep and as broad as a large city. Many scientists believe that just such an impact 65 million years ago led to the extinction of the dinosaurs.

We had one near miss on August 10, 1972, but this bright meteor, or bolide, was not a giant. Thousands of people saw a bright streak of light blaze a path in broad daylight through the sky over the United States and Canada. It whizzed on out of our atmosphere again, but it had come as low as 60 kilometers and created **sonic booms**. Based on factors such as speed and brightness, some scientists estimated that the object measured 10 meters across and weighed 1,000 tons.

intersect (in·tuhr·**sekt**)—to cross

catastrophic (kat·uh·**strof**·ik)—causing great damage

sonic booms (**son**·ik boomz)—loud noises caused by objects traveling faster than the speed of sound

Where did these rocks and metal chunks the size of footballs, houses, and mountains come from originally? Astronomers used to think that early in the history of the solar system there was a planet in the gap between Mars and Jupiter. Gradually the planet was pulled so close to Jupiter that Jupiter's powerful gravitation shattered the smaller planet, breaking it up into the asteroids. Now they think that the asteroids may be chunks of rock and metal left over from the time the planets were being formed. Jupiter's gravitation, they say, prevented the asteroid fragments from ever collecting into planet-size objects.

Messengers From Space

On the night of November 13, 1833, a shower of meteors lighted up the sky. "The stars fell like flakes of snow," said one observer. Others, also believing that meteors were falling stars, thought that no stars would be left in the sky the next night.

Away from the city lights on any clear night you can see about five "falling stars" in an hour. They are not stars, of course, but lumps of rock and metal which range from the size of dust grains to—once every several thousand years—a rare piece more than 10 meters across. When they are in space these objects are called *meteoroids*. Most of them probably come from the asteroid belt. When one enters Earth's atmosphere at a speed from 15 to 72 kilometers a second it burns up from **frictional** heating and glows as the quick streak of light that we call a *meteor*. If it survives the hot journey through the atmosphere and strikes the ground, we call it a *meteorite*.

frictional (frik·shuhn·l]— heat caused by objects rubbing against each other

These children are standing next to one of the largest meteorites in the world.

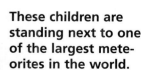

Namibia
(nuh•**mib**•ee•uh)—
a country in southwest
Africa

magnolia
(mag•**nohl**•yuh)—
a fragrant, flowering
plant

Every day meteorites plunge to Earth and add at least a quarter of a ton to our planet's mass. The largest meteorite found on Earth is in **Namibia**. It weighs some 60 tons. The next largest, about 30 tons, is on display at the American Museum of Natural History in New York. Another 10 tons a day are added by space-dust particles called *micrometeorites*, which are captured by Earth's magnetic field and float gently to the ground. Some of these have even been found on the petals of flowers. If you are lucky, someday you might find a micrometeorite on a **magnolia**.

Sporadic meteors are the ones we see on just about any night, falling out of the sky from any direction. But others, the *shower* meteors, seem to travel in swarms. The swarms return year after year and shower down on us at the rate of about 60 an hour from certain parts of the sky. Those showers that seem to come out of the constellation Leo are called *Leonids;* those coming from the direction of Orion are called the *Orionids;* and those we see in the constellation Gemini are called *Geminids.*

Shower meteors seem to radiate toward us from a point in a particular constellation, but this is an illusion. Actually, they travel in parallel lines, just as snowflakes fall in more or less parallel lines but appear to radiate from a particular point as we see them through the windshield of a moving car. Also, we see more snowflakes ahead of us, through the windshield, than when we look through the rear window. Likewise, we see more meteors when we look in the direction of Earth's orbital motion—Earth's "windshield"—than when we look "back." This happens, in our daily rotation, between midnight and noon, so the best times for meteor watching are the dark hours between midnight and dawn.

The Leonid meteor shower in 1966

The Role of Comets

Astronomers think that most shower meteors are debris from comets. The Leonid and Perseid showers of late summer are probably the remains of comet tails. And the Orionid shower may be dust left from past appearances of Halley's Comet. The Infrared Astronomical Satellite (IRAS) added a new element to this idea when it found an asteroid whose orbit crosses planet Mercury's. The asteroid's orbit looks like that of a comet, and scientists soon discovered that the asteroid's path **coincides** exactly with the orbit followed by the Geminid shower meteors. Does that mean the Geminid shower is due to an asteroid instead of to a comet? Or does it mean that the new "asteroid" is actually a burned-out comet, as certain Earth-crossers might be? If so, the Geminids also come from a comet.

coincides (koh·in·**siedz**)— is exactly the same

Astronomers have studied comets for generations.

Classes of Meteorites

If meteoroids and asteroids really did form at the same time as the planets, we would expect to find them made of some of the same materials as the planets. And this is just what we do find. There are three classes of meteorites—iron, stony, and the stony-irons. The irons are a blend of iron and nickel. The stony meteorites are mostly silicate rock with a little iron and nickel. Midway between the irons and stony meteorites are the stony-irons, made up of about half stone and half metal.

Most meteorites found on Earth are stony, as are about 90 percent of those that fall through space. But the stony meteorites, once on the ground, are harder to recognize than the irons. They also decay faster—both during their passage through the atmosphere and because **erosion** attacks them once they land. The irons are tougher but, since they are so outnumbered, we find fewer of them.

erosion (i·**roh**·zhuhn)— damage caused by wind, rain, or acid

Put Your Habits to Work in

Literature	Social Studies	Science	Math

Before I Read Habit:
Decide what I need to know.

Before you read a chapter in your science text-book, look at the title, heads, introduction, summary, and diagrams to decide what the author wants you to understand.

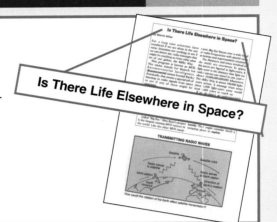

Is There Life Elsewhere in Space?

While I Read Habit:
Stop and ask, "How does it connect to what I know?"

Stop and ask yourself how what you're read-ing connects to what you know. One way to do this is to jot a note about how what the author is telling you connects to what you already know.

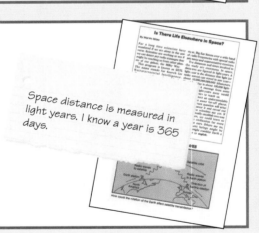

Space distance is measured in light years. I know a year is 365 days.

After I Read Habit:
React to what I've read.

When reading your science textbook, you can react to what you've read by deciding whether the key points make sense. You can also decide where you can go to check the facts.

I could check a CD-Rom at the library.

You may wish to use the **Put Your Habits to Work Sheet** (page 17 in your *Strategy Practice Book*) to practice these habits in your other reading.

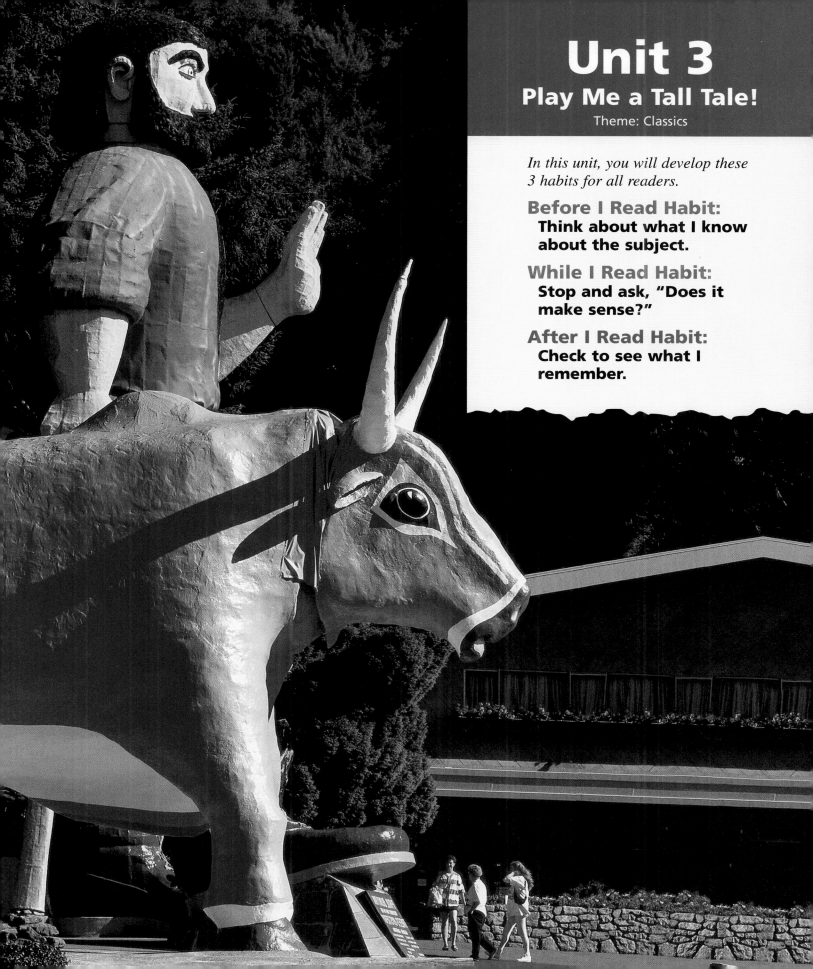

Unit 3
Play Me a Tall Tale!
Theme: Classics

In this unit, you will develop these 3 habits for all readers.

Before I Read Habit:
Think about what I know about the subject.

While I Read Habit:
Stop and ask, "Does it make sense?"

After I Read Habit:
Check to see what I remember.

Learn 3 of the 9 Habits

In this unit, you will develop three habits—one for before you read, one for while you are reading, and one for after you finish reading. Start with **Before I Read**. Read the habit and strategy. Then read my notes below.

Before I Read

Which **HABIT** will I learn?

Think about what I know about the subject.
If I develop this habit, I will bring to mind what I already know about the subject. This gets me ready to connect what I read to what I know so I will understand it better.

Which **STRATEGY** will I use to learn this habit?
Identify the genre and decide what I know about this genre.

My Notes

• Strategy says to identify the genre. Genre is a kind of writing like a novel, a short story, a poem, or a play.

• Look at the selection. I see the names of speakers and words like "Scene One." It looks a lot like a script for a play.

• I think this is a play, but I don't see any descriptions of scenes. This must be a play where the characters just read their lines from a script.

John Henry

Scene One

NARRATOR: People have said that on the night that John Henry was born, the earth trembled, and the Mississippi River reversed direction and ran upstream! Some say that John Henry grew to be more than seven feet tall, and that he had the strength of 30 men. According to legend, John Henry was born with a hammer in his hand. It was only natural that he became a steel-driving man for the railroad. Now, back in those days, men built the railroads with their own hands, not with machines. They dug tunnels through mountains and built bridges over rivers. They laid miles and miles of track by hand. One day, exciting news spread throughout the camp where John Henry was working.

JAKE: (excited) Hey, John Henry, did you hear the news? The railroad wants men for work on the Big Bend Tunnel, and they're payin' twice the usual rate!

TOM: (sneering) Yeah, twice the usual rate—and a hundred times the danger! I just think I'll stay right here.

JOHN HENRY: Well, I reckon I'll just have to see about that tunnel.

Now read the habit and strategy for **While I Read**. When you see ❓, read my notes in the margin.

While I Read

Which **HABIT** will I learn?

> **Stop and ask, "Does it make sense?"**
> If I develop this habit, I will stop now and then to make sure I understand what I'm reading.

Which **STRATEGY** will I use to learn this habit?

> Decide whether what I've read fits with what I know about the characters.

shaker and turners (**shay**·kuhr and **turn**·uhrz)—workers who shake and then turn a steel pick between hammer hits to break up rock

 Stop and Ask

Does it make sense? Decide whether what I've read fits with what I know about the characters.

I think John Henry wants to try to drive—or dig out—the tunnel. I know he's strong, so that makes sense.

Scene Two

NARRATOR: Thousands of men and boys came to West Virginia from near and far to help dig the Big Bend Tunnel for the Chesapeake and Ohio Railroad. A lot of helpers were needed—boys to carry water and tools to the workers, blacksmiths to sharpen the drills that would cut deep into the mountain, men to set the dynamite that would blast great chunks of rock from the mountain's face, and **shaker and turners** to hold the steel drills firmly against the rock. Steel-drivers—the men who drove the long, sharp drills into the rock with mighty blows of their heavy hammers—were also needed. John Henry came to the mountain with his hammer in his hand.

HARRY: (awed) That is one big mountain!

SAM: (discouraged) No use even *tryin'* to dig a tunnel through that mountain. It's solid rock! No one's ever goin' to drive a tunnel through that mountain!

SEVERAL VOICES: Uh-uh. No way. Can't be done. Might as well go home, boys.

JOHN HENRY: Who says it's no use even tryin' to drive a tunnel through that mountain? ❓ *Strategy Alert!*

SAM: (softly) I said that.

JOHN HENRY: Who are you, and what are you here to do?

SAM: My name's Sam. I'm a shaker and turner, and that's what I came here to do. But that mountain. (pauses) I just guess I'll be a water boy instead. I can't drive steel through that mountain.

JOHN HENRY: (firmly) Well, I can, and I will! And you will, too, Sam. We're goin' to drive a tunnel right straight through that mountain!

SAM: (protesting) Naw, I can't do that. You're a big man, John Henry. Sure, you can drive steel through that mountain—or through any mountain. But I can't. I'm just a small man. I can't do the things a big man like you can do.

JOHN HENRY: Maybe so, Sam, but you listen to me. Sure, I'm big, and you're small. But think a minute about what a railroad engine looks like. Some of its wheels are big, and some of its wheels are small. They may not do the same work or carry the same load, but they all have a job to do. And that railroad engine wouldn't be able to run along the tracks without all those different size wheels doin' their own jobs. ❷ *Strategy Alert!*

Stop and Ask

Does it make sense? Decide whether what I've read fits with what I know about the characters.

● ● ● ● ● ● ● ● ● ●

Sam thinks he's too small to be much help. It makes sense that John Henry's story about the railroad engine would help Sam see that even a small person can help out.

Stop and Ask

Does it make sense? Decide whether what I've read fits with what I know about the characters.

Sam doesn't think he can be John's shaker. That makes sense because Sam doesn't think he can do much. John Henry keeps trying to give him a "pep talk."

arc (ahrk)—something shaped like a curve or an arch

SAM: Those wheels are made out of steel. I'm not made out of steel! I'm just a man.

JOHN HENRY: That's right. You're a man, and I'm a man, and a man is nothin' but a man. My size man does one kind of job, and your size man does another kind of job. And if we each just do the best job we can, we can drive a tunnel through that mountain! Now you come with me. You're goin' to be my shaker!

SAM: Naw, I can't be your shaker. You need a big man. **?** *Strategy Alert!*

JOHN HENRY: You're just the man I need, Sam. Now, you take this steel drill and hold the sharp end against the rock. When I hit it, just give it a shake. When I hit it again, turn it. Just keep on doin' that, and we'll get along just fine. You'll see.

NARRATOR: Sam took the long steel drill from John Henry and held it against the mountain. John Henry drew back his huge hammer and swung it in a wide **arc**. It landed on the drill with a mighty CLANG!

[Sound effect: hammer hitting steel]

NARRATOR: Sam turned the drill, and John Henry swung his hammer.

[Sound effect: hammer hitting steel]

NARRATOR: With John Henry and Sam at the head, the men fell to work driving the Big Bend Tunnel through the mountain.

Scene Three

NARRATOR: The work of driving the tunnel went on and on and on. With every blow of John Henry's hammer, rock chips flew. Bit by bit, the tunnel burrowed through the rock. Deep inside the mountain, candles and oil lamps fought the darkness as the men worked. The deeper they went, the more dangerous the work became. Many men, weakened by the dust and smoke inside the tunnel, fell by the way. Men died when falling rock crashed on them from above. Still the work went on. As they worked, the men sang to keep up their spirits and to set a rhythm for the hammers. Then one day there was a low rumble and the sound of falling stones.

[Sound effects: low rumble, stones striking on rock]

HARRY: (fearfully) Listen! Did you hear that?

NARRATOR: The men stopped singing, and their hammers fell silent as they listened. The dreadful noise came again.

[Sound effect: louder rumble]

WILL: (panicking) It's a cave-in! Let's get out of here!

MACK: (hopefully) Maybe it's not near us. Maybe we'll be okay.

HARRY: I'm not waitin' to find out, boys! I'm gettin' out now!

Stop and Ask

Does it make sense? Decide whether what I've read fits with what I know about the characters.

John Henry didn't run out. He's saving the men! That makes sense because he is a caring person. He showed that when he talked with Sam and made friends with him.

NARRATOR: Then came a sharp noise and a rumbling just above where the men were working. They looked up in horror as the tunnel roof cracked open and small stones began to **pelt** them.

[Sound effects: loud rumble, stones falling]

JONAS: (shouting) Run for it, boys!

SEVERAL VOICES: (shouting, panicked) Hurry! Run! Get out of here! Move, move, move!

JOHN HENRY: (shouting) It's too late, men! There's no time! The whole roof's comin' down! Duck down low!

NARRATOR: Directly above the men, a huge slab of rock broke loose from the tunnel roof. The men fell to the ground in fear, covering their heads with their arms. John Henry stood tall and raised himself to his full height, reaching up his mighty arms. As the giant rock slab fell, John Henry bent his head and took the full weight of the rock on his arms and back. His body bent under the **tremendous** weight. For a moment, all seemed lost. Then John Henry gathered all his strength and stood firmly in place, holding the rock slab above the frightened men.

JOHN HENRY: I've got it! Get out of here now! Go! ❓ *Strategy Alert!*

NARRATOR: The men fled from under the rock, but they didn't leave John Henry there. They returned with huge **timbers** and placed them under one end of the slab to prop it up. John Henry crouched and lowered the other end to the ground. The men held their breath while, for a long moment, John Henry didn't move.

JONAS: (worriedly) He isn't movin'! Why isn't he movin'?

SAM: (worriedly) John Henry, are you okay?

JOHN HENRY: (sighing) I sure am glad to get that rock off my back! Yeah, yeah, I'm just fine, Sam, just fine.

SAM: Why aren't you comin' out from under that rock, John Henry? You sure you're all right?

MACK: You need a hand, John Henry?

JOHN HENRY: Naw, naw, boys. I just don't seem able to move my feet. I don't know what's wrong. Other than that, I'm just fine. (grunts) Oof—there, I'm okay now.

NARRATOR: When he had crawled out from under the rock, the men took John Henry's hands and pulled him to his feet. *Strategy Alert!*

HARRY: (awed) I never saw anyone do anythin' like that before, John Henry! I was sure you were a goner!

MACK: I was sure we were all goners!

timbers (**tim**·buhrs)— cut logs

Stop and Ask ❓

Does it make sense? Decide whether what I've read fits with what I know about the characters.

· · · · · · · · ·

It says that John Henry can't move his feet and that the other men had to help him. That doesn't make sense because John is so strong. No one had to help him before.

Stop and Ask

Does it make sense? Decide whether what I've read fits with what I know about the characters.

· · · · · · · · · · · ·

John Henry left his footprints in the rock. That doesn't make sense because no one can do that! On the other hand, he was very strong, but it must be an exaggeration. After all, this is a tall tale.

WILL: What can we do for you, John Henry? Are you really okay? How do you feel?

JOHN HENRY: Just help me find my hammer, boys. How about bringin' those lights closer?

NARRATOR: The men brought the lights closer, while John Henry looked around the tunnel floor for his hammer.

JOHN HENRY: Thanks. I see it, boys.

NARRATOR: John Henry picked up his hammer and turned to go to the tunnel heading. However, the other men didn't move. They were rooted to the spot, staring at the place where John Henry had stood, holding up the slab of rock.

HARRY: (awed) I've never seen anythin' like that before! Never!

WILL: Well, you never saw anyone hold up a heavy weight like that before!

JONAS: (unbelieving) It can't be. It just can't be!

SAM: I can't believe my eyes!

MACK: Well, seein' is believin', boys. John sank right up to his ankles in solid rock! That slab was so heavy John Henry sank right down into the floor! Look at his footprints in the rock! 🕐 *Strategy Alert!*

SAM: So that's why he couldn't move his feet!

JOHN HENRY: Come on, boys, what're you standin' there for? We've got to drive a tunnel through this mountain!

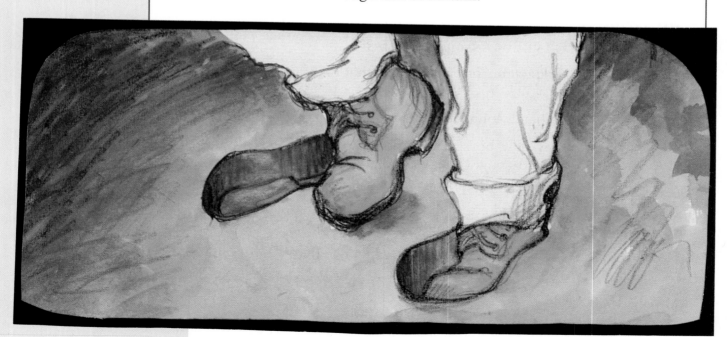

Congratulations! You finished reading. Now read the habit and strategy for **After I Read**. Then read my notes below.

After I Read

Which **HABIT** will I learn?
Check to see what I remember.
If I develop this habit, I will check to see what I remember as soon as I finish reading. It helps me see if I really understood what I read and helps me remember it better, too.

Which **STRATEGY** will I use to learn this habit?
Decide why I made certain inferences about characters and events.

My Notes

- Strategy says to decide why I made some inferences. That means to decide why I thought certain things about characters and events even though the story didn't actually say those things.

- The story focused on how strong John Henry was, but I think he was a really kind man, too. His actions—like the way he treated Sam and his bravery in the cave-in—showed he cared about others.

- John was smart, too. He helped Sam to see that it takes all kinds of people to do a job well.

Now it's time to practice the three habits and strategies you learned when you read "John Henry." Start with **Before I Read**. Look at the box below. It should look familiar! Reread the habit you will practice. Reread the strategy you will use—then do it!

Before I Read

Which **HABIT** will I practice?
Think about what I know about the subject.
If I develop this habit, I will bring to mind what I already know about the subject. This gets me ready to connect what I read to what I know so I will understand it better.

Which **STRATEGY** will I use to practice this habit?
Identify the genre and decide what I know about this genre.

 Use the **Before I Read Strategy Sheet** for "The Problem With Pa's Peppers" (page 18 in your *Strategy Practice Book*) to help you think about what you know about the subject.

The Problem With Pa's Peppers

Scene One

NARRATOR: It was a day like any other. Pa Perkins was out early working in the fields. Ma had breakfast on the table for herself and the children—older sister Marnie, older brother Luke, younger brother Billy, and younger sister Ruby. And like any other day, nobody was very interested in eating Pa's sausages. You see, the peppers in them were mild and flavorless, and, well, so were the sausages.

RUBY: Ma, why can't Pa grow good hot peppers?

MA: I wish I knew, little Ruby. Seems like anybody with a stick can grow a pepper with some kick. Pa does everything just like other folks. But their peppers grow up big, red, and **zesty**. Pa's just grow up!

zesty (**zes**·tee)—flavorful; interesting

NARRATOR: You see, mountain folks needed good hot peppers. Fresh meat required red pepper to preserve it for the winter. And what good was a crock of bacon and bean soup without some good hot pepper vinegar?

Read the habit and strategy below. Look for the *Strategy Alerts!* as you continue to read.

While I Read

Which **HABIT** will I practice?

Stop and ask, "Does it make sense?"
If I develop this habit, I will stop now and then to make sure I understand what I'm reading.

Which **STRATEGY** will I use to practice this habit?
Decide whether what I've read fits with what I know about the characters.

 Use the **While I Read Strategy Sheet** for "The Problem With Pa's Peppers" (page 19 in your *Strategy Practice Book*) as you read.

vexes (**veks**·ez)— disturbs; annoys

LUKE: I guess poor peppers must put Pa out of sorts.

MA: No they don't. Nothing ever **vexes** your pa. He's the mildest man I ever laid eyes on.

BILLY: If Mr. Grady's pepper crop turned out the way ours does, he'd be yelling and kicking up a dusty fuss about it. Mr. Brown, too.

tantrum (**tan**·trum)— a fit of bad temper

MA: And Mr. Horner. He'd be having a **tantrum**! But not your pa. He hasn't lost his temper in all the years I've known him.

MARNIE: (in a loud whisper) Listen, Ma, I know Pa is looking to plant the new pepper crop tomorrow. Why don't you go see Old Granny down in the valley? I hear she's strange, but people say she knows things. Why don't you go down there and ask Old Granny why Pa can't grow good peppers?

MA: (after a pause) Well, I've tried everything else. I suppose it wouldn't do any harm.

NARRATOR: So Ma put together a gift basket of biscuits and jam she'd made the day before, and she went down into the valley below.

Scene Two

NARRATOR: That night, while Pa was washing up, Ma and the children were preparing the dinner table.

BILLY: (whispering) What did Old Granny say, Ma?

MARNIE: Did she tell you about a special **concoction**?

RUBY: Did she give you a powerful **potion**?

LUKE: Tell us what she said.

MA: (whispering) Well, first she asked if Pa was a mild man, and I told her, yes, he's never lost his temper because he's got no temper to lose. And she said a mild man can only grow mild peppers. It takes a hot-tempered man to raise hot peppers. Quiet now, here comes your pa. Strategy Alert!

MARNIE: (very quietly) Is there anything to be done about it?

MA: You'll find out soon enough.

PA: I'm going to plant the pepper crop early tomorrow morning. We ought to get out there before the sun comes up. Maybe if we get those plants in before the sunshine gets to them, that old sun won't have a chance to steal the heat from them.

concoction
(kon·**kok**·shun)—
mixture or recipe

potion (**poh**·shuhn)—
a drink that is supposed
to have special powers

Stop and Ask ?

Does it make sense?
Decide whether
what I've read fits
with what I know
about the characters.

Scene Three

NARRATOR: Before dawn, Ma snuck out of bed and made preparations. She started in the parlor where they all slept in the summertime. Then she crept into the kitchen and finally out on the porch. There was so very much to do and very little time to do it!

[Sound effect: rooster crowing]

PA: Ma! **Young'uns**! Get up! We got to get an early start on those peppers.

NARRATOR: Pa jumped out of bed and tried to pull on his trousers.

PA: Now what's going on here? I can't get my leg through.

MARNIE: What's wrong, Pa?

NARRATOR: Pa was hopping around, trying to push his foot through his trouser leg. When one foot wouldn't push through, Pa tried the other, but that didn't work either.

RUBY: (laughing) Why's Pa hopping around?

MARNIE: Look! Somebody's tied a tight knot in the bottom of Pa's trouser legs!

PA: (calmly) This is no time to be playing games. I haven't got time to be sitting here untying knots.

BILLY: We didn't do it, Pa, honest!

young'uns (**yung**·nz)— children

PA: All right, all right. Come on along now. We've got peppers to plant.

Stop and Ask

Does it make sense? Decide whether what I've read fits with what I know about the characters.

❓ *Strategy Alert!*

NARRATOR: Pa put his feet into his shoes and stood up.

PA: Now what's the matter here? I can't get my feet off of the floor. I can't even move them! Something's happened to my feet. Ouch!

NARRATOR: Pa pulled so hard that one of his feet came out of his shoe, and his knee came up and crashed into his chin.

PA: Praise be! I'm not **paralyzed** after all! You ought to have more respect for your pa than to nail his shoes to the floor.

paralyzed (**par**·uh·liezd)—unable to move

LUKE: But, Pa, we didn't do it, and we don't know who did.

PA: Well . . . all right, all right. Ma! It's time to get moving. We've got to have breakfast.

MA: I'm too sleepy. Get in there and cook your own. ❓ *Strategy Alert!*

Stop and Ask

Does it make sense? Decide whether what I've read fits with what I know about the characters.

NARRATOR: Pa began to look a little out of humor, but not nearly so much as after his first swallow of coffee.

PA: Who put the salt in the sugar bowl?

RUBY: We didn't do it, Pa!

LUKE: We don't know who did it, Pa. Honest!

PA: Well I certainly didn't! Hmph! All right, never mind. Look how late it is. We've got to get going.

dumbstruck
(**dum**·struk)—unable to
speak

pratfall (**prat**·fawl)—
a fall backwards on the
backside

switch (swich)—a small
stick

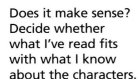

Stop and Ask ?

Does it make sense?
Decide whether
what I've read fits
with what I know
about the characters.

NARRATOR: But as Pa pushed open the kitchen door [Sound effect: water splashing], a bucketful of cold water tumbled down from above. The children stood there for a moment, **dumbstruck**.

RUBY: Pa, you look so funny, just like kitty after her bath!

PA: Hmph!

NARRATOR: Pa changed his clothes and charged out of the house. But as he stepped off the porch . . .

[Sound effect: **pratfall**]

LUKE: (laughing) Who took the plank out of the bottom step?

PA: Do you think this is funny?

NARRATOR: Pa grabbed a **switch** from a dogwood tree beside the door.

MA: Run, children! Get away!

NARRATOR: And run they did, but Pa ran after them.

PA: I'll teach you to play pranks on me! ? *Strategy Alert!*

MA: Now, Pa, no time for that! You've got peppers to plant.

PA: All right, we'll forget about this for now. But you kids will get a talking to later. Now grab those hoes.

NARRATOR: So Pa and the children set to work, up and down the rows, hoeing and planting, hoeing and planting. The sun was hot, nobody had eaten breakfast, and everybody began to feel cranky.

RUBY: I'm tired, Pa!

BILLY: I'm hungry!

LUKE: It's just plain too hot!

PA: Be quiet! We'll keep right on working till we're done.

NARRATOR: At long last, they had finished. They all crouched and lay down their hoes. Pa brightened a bit. The peppers were in and he began to feel better.

[Sound effect: snorting hogs]

PA: What's that?

LUKE: The hogs are loose! They're digging up the pepper plants!

RUBY: They're everywhere!

PA: Get away, you nasty hogs!

NARRATOR: Pa was swinging his hoe like a wild man, but the hogs were too fast. They ran around, squealing and tearing up the newly planted field, looking for a way out.

BILLY: We'll help, Pa!

NARRATOR: The children tried but ended up **riling** the hogs even further. After a while, Ma came along and led the hogs to the open place in the fence where she had let them in.

MA: Well, you sure have made a mess of the pepper patch!

riling (**riel**·ing)—
annoying; irritating

NARRATOR: Pa turned to Ma, and for a moment he just stared at her. The children thought they saw smoke coming out of his ears. And if you sniffed the air, you might have thought something was burning. Then Pa grabbed his hoe, and stared at the children. They didn't need to be told even once. They all started hoeing again. Ma helped, too, this time. And when they were finished planting the field a second time, they all went back to the house for a pitcher of cold buttermilk. (pause) And how did those peppers finally turn out? Well, *everybody* agreed that Pa's peppers were the hottest ever grown in those mountains.

(All readers mime eating sausages that are really *good* and really *hot*.)

LUKE: Whew! Those peppers sure grew up mighty high and hot.

MA: Now, Billy and Ruby, don't you go into that pepper patch. You might get burned!

BILLY: When it rained this morning, I could hear the water sizzling in the pepper patch.

MA: Last night those peppers lit up the field. Pa, don't forget your fire **tongs** when you go out later to pick us some for dinner.

NARRATOR: And when the sausages were finally made in the wintertime, there never were such tasty red hot sausages. And that's how Ma solved the problem with Pa's peppers. *Strategy Alert!*

tongs (tawngz)—a tool for gripping and lifting something

Stop and Ask ?

Does it make sense? Decide whether what I've read fits with what I know about the characters.

Now that you've finished reading, review the **After I Read** habit below. Think about what you read in "The Problem With Pa's Peppers" as you practice the strategy.

After I Read

Which **HABIT** will I practice?
Check to see what I remember.
If I develop this habit, I will check to see what I remember as soon as I finish reading. It helps me see if I really understood what I read and helps me remember it better, too.

Which **STRATEGY** will I use to practice this habit?
Decide why I made certain inferences about characters and events.

Use the **After I Read Strategy Sheet** for "The Problem With Pa's Peppers" (page 20 in your *Strategy Practice Book*) to check to see what you remember.

Now read "Eli and Fetch" and apply these habits and strategies.

Before I Read

Which **HABIT** will I apply?
Think about what I know about the subject.

Which **STRATEGY** will I use to apply this habit?
Identify the genre and decide what I know about this genre.

While I Read

Which **HABIT** will I apply?
Stop and ask, "Does it make sense?"

Which **STRATEGY** will I use to apply this habit?
Decide whether what I've read fits with what I know about the characters.

After I Read

Which **HABIT** will I apply?
Check to see what I remember.

Which **STRATEGY** will I use to apply this habit?
Decide why I made certain inferences about characters and events.

Use the **Self-Assessment Sheet** for "Eli and Fetch" (pages 21 and 22 in your *Strategy Practice Book*) as you read to see how well you can apply the habits and strategies.

Eli and Fetch

Scene One

NARRATOR: The thaw came late to Bartlett's Ridge that year a long time ago. Young Eli had promised himself and his dog Fetch a trip to Riverhead that spring. And he was eager to get there before the spring planting.

ELI: (excitedly) They got this train called the Whistlin' Wind that goes tearing along the banks of the Skarlee River. Aw, Fetch, some folks who've been there at night say it flies out of the dark like a screaming teakettle. And Jeb Kerwald came back last week sayin' he seen it blow through the river mist like a hissing water moccasin with one glaring eye above its nose.

NARRATOR: Making that 20-mile journey was all Eli could think about. But the more he thought about it, the less easy he felt about taking his dog along.

ELI: (with concern) Fetch, people say this train-critter is a loco . . . loco . . . somethin'. I'm afraid you'll get so scared you might run away.

NARRATOR: So Eli decided it would be best to leave Fetch with a neighbor. Kyle Kench and his brother Merton seemed like a good choice.

ELI: They never go anywhere. And their cabin is down the mountain on the way to Riverhead.

tufts—clumps of hair

NARRATOR: A few days later, Eli and Fetch made their way to the Kench cabin. Eli unhooked the gate leading to their door. Two bald heads with **tufts** of rusty-colored hair bobbed fearfully out from behind the shutters.

ELI: It's just me, Eli.

reproachfully
(ri·**prohch**·fuhl·lee)—
in a scolding way

MERTON: (**reproachfully**) Didn't your people teach you to yell before entering the yard? Where's your manners, boy?

ELI: Yes, sirs, I'll give a holler the next time. You can be sure of that. Anyway, I'm off to Riverhead for a few days. I come to ask a favor.

MERTON: (coldly) Favor? Kenches don't do favors.

KYLE: Why're you going there?

ELI: I'm going to see the Whistlin' Wind at full speed.

KYLE: (sneering) Well, if that's all you're going for, then fool's speed to you, too.

ELI: (hopefully) I'd pay you something to leave Fetch with you while I'm gone.

NARRATOR: At that, the Kenches froze stock-still. Their only moving parts were their eyeballs, which shifted to each other and then back to Eli as if sharing the same thought.

KYLE: Pay us? Nonsense. We'd love to have old Fetch stay with us.

MERTON: (overly sweet) Why, we'll treat him just like family.

ELI: (gratefully) Aw, that's swell. Much **obliged,** fellas. Hey-o, Fetch, come here, boy.

obliged (uh·**bliejd**)— grateful

NARRATOR: Eli gave Fetch a pat and a wink. Fetch winked back. After a flurry of hand waving by all and a paw wave from Fetch, Eli was out the gate and off to see the Whistlin' Wind. In all his eagerness, he paid no attention to the loud whoop coming from the cabin as the door slammed shut.

Scene Two

NARRATOR: A few days later, Eli was at the Kenches' gate once again.

ELI: (excitedly) Yo there, Mr. Kench! Hey-o and a-yo there! It's me, Eli!

NARRATOR: The cabin door opened and a fuzzy bald head popped out.

KYLE: Why look at you, all ruddy-faced and muddy-shoed. It's a mighty sloppy **trek** back from Riverhead, isn't it?

trek—a difficult journey

ELI: Yeah, cold too. But it sure was worth the trip.

KYLE: (casually) Reckon it was. You come by sometime and tell us about it.

ELI: (fearfully) Whoa there a second. I come for Fetch. Where is he?

KYLE: Fetch? Now wait a minute. Merton, he's asking about his dog.

MERTON: Yeah, we're sorry for what happened. He was a good one.

ELI: (in a panic) What happened? What's wrong? He didn't run away, did he?

MERTON: Nah.

ELI: (worriedly) He isn't hurt, is he?

NARRATOR: Just like two days earlier, the brothers froze for a moment, their eyeballs shifting to each other and back to Eli.

KYLE: (somberly) Well, boy, truth to tell, he's deader than that spruce over there that got felled in that storm last summer.

MERTON: Yep, he's as dead as dead can be.

KYLE: Eaten by **chigger** bugs.

MERTON: We put Fetch up in that rental shack by the pond. Last summer, as **mangy** a group as ever you saw left that place a terrible mess and chockful of chigger bugs. Well, those chiggers got to poor Fetch at night and all that's left is a scattering of bones.

ELI: (sadly) Oh, poor Fetch. I'd as soon those bugs had eaten me instead.

NARRATOR: Eli stumbled through the gate and sadly made his way up the road toward home. But something didn't seem quite right. So, after thinking awhile, Eli stalked back to the Kenches' old cabin.

ELI: (calmly) Kyle. Merton. I'm just so flat out and feeling so bad. I don't think I can make it all the way up that steep trail on these two sore feet. Could you lend me your mule till tomorrow morning?

chigger (**chig**·uhr)— a tiny six-legged bug

mangy (**mayn**·jee)— dirty; shabby

KYLE: You want Horace? I just don't know, boy. We'll be plowing this week and needing Horace every day.

ELI: (**assertively**) Then you got to let me spend the night here with you boys. There's no way I'll make that last half a mile.

NARRATOR: Once again the brothers stood stock-still, eyes shiftin' to and fro.

MERTON: (after a pause) Now, Kyle, I'm sure we can do without old Horace till tomorrow. You will bring him back sunup tomorrow, Eli?

ELI: (earnestly) You have my word, sir.

NARRATOR: So Merton brought Horace to Eli, and Horace took Eli home.

assertively
(uh·**sur**·tiv·lee)—
confidently; boldly

Scene Three

NARRATOR: Well, Eli's word was about all they had because many days passed without any sign of their mule. And neither of the Kenches were in any shape to trek up the steep slope to Eli's house.

KYLE: (angrily) We've been **hoodwinked**! That scoundrel stole our mule. Why, we'll drag him into jail. He'll pay dearly for every day Horace ain't behind that plow . . . . What the . . . Who's that?

MERTON: By golly, it's Eli!

ELI: Hey-o and a-yo there, y'all. Thought you might like to hear about my trip to Riverhead and the great Whistlin' Wind.

MERTON: We'd like to know where you been with Horace. (pause) Hold on now. You don't got him with you?

ELI: (casually) Horace? Now wait a minute. You asking about your mule? Oh, well, I'm sorry for what happened. He was a good one.

hoodwinked
(**hud**·wingk'd)—tricked

hoosegow (**hoos·**gow)—
jail

hokum (**hoh·**kuhm)—
nonsense

gaggle (**gag·**uhl)—
a cluster or group

KYLE: (angrily) Why you rascal. You gone and lost him, haven't you?

ELI: No, he's not exactly lost.

MERTON: (in a panic) You haven't killed him, have you?

ELI: Well, I'm not certain, but I'd guess he is about as dead as that tree over there that was struck by lightning.

KYLE: Aw fiddle-faddle! You're coming with us to Sheriff Dewey. He'll haul you into the **hoosegow** for stealing our mule.

NARRATOR: A few minutes later, Eli sat calmly in Sheriff Dewey's office as the Kenches raged about how they'd been robbed.

KYLE: (accusingly) The boy's a mule-thief and anything else he says is just **hokum**!

SHERIFF: Calm down, Kyle. There're two sides to any squabble and I've only heard but one. What do you have to say, Eli?

ELI: Well, I never saw anything like it. There I am atop old Horace headin' to home. And this **gaggle** of turkey buzzards comes circling. Being as tired as I am, I don't notice them getting lower and closer. But soon as I look up, there's one breathing in my ear. He's so close, I can hear his stomach gurglin'. Then, in a flash, that buzzard ducks down behind and grabs Horace's tail. The next thing I know, I'm tumbling head over heels and Horace is sailing skyward. And all of them mean old buzzards are laughing like hyenas.

SHERIFF: (patiently) Now, Eli, I want you to hang on just one minute. (pause) In all my days I never heard a turkey buzzard laugh like a hyena.

ELI: I figure it had been slim pickin's for those buzzards all winter and they were powerful hungry. Anyway, they flew off yonder with poor Horace a-braying in the wind. I reckon there ain't nothing left of him now but some dry bones and a few tufts of donkey hair.

MERTON: (in disbelief) Did'ya ever hear such a crock of **hogwash** in your life?

hogwash (**hog**·wosh)— foolishness; nonsense

SHERIFF: Well, fellas, if a big old hound dog could be eaten by a swarm of hungry chiggers, then a pack of starving turkey buzzards could take off with a mule and polish him off, too.

NARRATOR: This stopped the Kench boys cold. And no matter where their eyes shifted, there was no escaping the truth.

ELI: Of course, if my Fetch can come back to me after being **devoured** by chiggers, there's no reason old Horace can't come back after being picked clean by buzzards.

devoured (di·**vowrd**)— gobbled up; ate

NARRATOR: And that's just what happened. The next day, Kyle and Merton had Horace back behind the plow, and Eli and Fetch went a-fetchin'.

Put Your Habits to Work in

Literature	Social Studies	Science	Math

Before I Read Habit:
Think about what I know about the subject.

Remember to identify the genre of the literature you are reading. The genre means the kind of writing—play, short story, etc. Then decide what you know about the genre.

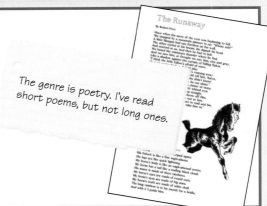

The genre is poetry. I've read short poems, but not long ones.

While I Read Habit:
Stop and ask, "Does it make sense?"

When you read a story, don't forget to stop and ask yourself if what you're reading makes sense. Does what you've read fit with what you know about the characters?

He's running away.

After I Read Habit:
Check to see what I remember.

After you read, check to see what you remember. One way to do that is to think about the inferences you made about characters and events and your reasons for making them.

I knew the colt was scared because…

You may wish to use the **Put Your Habits to Work Sheet** (page 23 in your *Strategy Practice Book*) to practice these habits in your other reading.

Unit 4
Unsolved Mysteries in Medicine
Theme: Mystery

In this unit, you will develop these 3 habits for all readers.

Before I Read Habit:
Decide what I need to know.

While I Read Habit:
Stop and ask, "If it doesn't make sense, what can I do?"

After I Read Habit:
Use what I've read.

In this unit, you will develop three habits—one for before you read, one for while you are reading, and one for after you finish reading. Start with **Before I Read**. Read the habit and strategy. Then read my notes below.

Before I Read

Which **HABIT** will I learn?
Decide what I need to know.
If I develop this habit, I will have a reason for reading. I will understand it better and remember more of what I read.

Which **STRATEGY** will I use to learn this habit?
Use graphic aids to ask purpose-setting questions.

My Notes

- Strategy says to use graphic aids to ask purpose-setting questions. These questions can help guide my reading. A graphic aid could be a chart, a photo, a diagram, or a map.

- Page 101 has a diagram that shows how some germs are spread. Another purpose-setting question could be: How are germs spread?

- There's a diagram on page 102. I never knew there were differences between bacteria and viruses. One question could be: How are viruses different from bacteria?

The Aztecs greet Hernando Cortez. This drawing is from a manuscript by Friar Diego Duran.

Viruses
The Tiniest Killers

In 1519, a Spanish explorer named Hernando Cortez landed in an area that is now part of Mexico. A year later, in 1520, thousands of Aztec Indians began fighting against Cortez and his 400 men. What happened next changed the course of history. The Aztecs had built a strong civilization. They were experienced warriors. The Aztecs should have been able to kill all the Spaniards. But they didn't. In fact, the Aztecs hardly fought the Spaniards at all. Cortez's troops were able to defeat the mighty Aztec nation. Cortez destroyed the Aztecs' capital city. He built Mexico City on its ruins.

How could this have happened? How could a few hundred soldiers defeat an entire empire?

Now read the habit and strategy for **While I Read**. When you see , read my notes in the margin.

While I Read

Which **HABIT** will I learn?

Stop and ask, "If it doesn't make sense, what can I do?"
If I develop this habit, I will stop and figure out what to do so what I'm reading makes sense. Then I can keep reading and not be lost.

Which **STRATEGY** will I use to learn this habit?
Scan to find clarifying information.

immunity
(i·**myoo**·ni·tee)—
the ability to resist a disease

A Virus Destroys an Army

The Aztecs were not really defeated by the Spanish army, but by a disease—smallpox. On the night of their defeat, smallpox had broken out in the city. It quickly killed the nephew of Montezuma, the Aztec emperor, and many other Aztecs.

The Spanish had grown up with smallpox. Most of the soldiers probably had it as children. If you survive smallpox, you won't get it again. This is called building up an **immunity**.

In the New World, however, smallpox was unknown. The Spanish first brought it across the Atlantic Ocean. The local population had no immunity against it. The disease had a disastrous effect on the Aztecs. Their warriors fell victim to the virus, and the nation was defeated. Over the course of many years, smallpox killed millions of the Indian population.

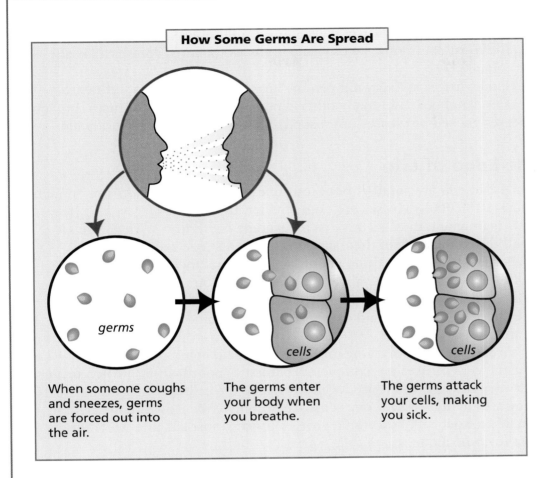

How Some Germs Are Spread

When someone coughs and sneezes, germs are forced out into the air.

germs

The germs enter your body when you breathe.

cells

The germs attack your cells, making you sick.

cells

What Is a Virus?

Until about 100 years ago, almost any disease-causing **organism** in humans was called a "virus." But as scientists learned what caused illnesses, they discovered that different types of pathogens [**path**·uh·juhnz], or disease carriers, cause different illnesses. Some, such as poisons, were easily identified. These included carbon monoxide, lead, mercury, arsenic, and potassium cyanide. Such chemicals destroy the body's **tissues** if they are breathed in or eaten.

Bacteria—microscopic living organisms—also were found to cause many diseases. These include strep throat, staph infections, and diphtheria [dip·**theer**·ee·uh]. Much of our early knowledge about bacteria was gained through the work of brilliant and courageous scientists. People such as Louis Pasteur, country doctor Robert Koch, and others learned how to combat bacteria with **antibiotics**. At first, it seemed that antibiotics could conquer all forms of disease.

Unfortunately, there was another, more **resistant** pathogen—the virus. So far, scientists have named more than 3,000 viruses. Of those, several hundred affect humans. ⑦ *Strategy Alert!*

organism (**or**·guh·niz·uhm)—any living thing

tissues (**tish**·ooz)— groups of cells that are somewhat alike

antibiotics (an·tee·bie·**ot**·iks)—group of medicines that destroy bacteria

resistant (ri·**zis**·tuhnt)— able to ward off

Stop and Ask ❓

If it doesn't make sense, what can I do? Scan to find clarifying information.

I don't understand what a pathogen is. I scanned the page and found that a pathogen is something that causes disease.

Fortunately, most viruses cause only a mild illness, or no illness at all. The most common type of virus produces the most common disease—the cold.

Some viruses are very dangerous, however. AIDS, rabies, influenza, measles, smallpox, and many other illnesses are caused by viruses. In fact, diseases caused by viruses are responsible for many deaths worldwide.

The Edge of Life

While bacteria are small—about four one-hundred thousandths of an inch (that's 4/100,000)—viruses are even smaller. In fact, the largest known virus is only one-third as large as an average bacterium. Viruses are so small that thousands of them can live inside a single cell!

Perhaps the oddest thing about viruses is that they exist on the edge of life. They are not quite alive. Yet they are not quite dead, either. Bacteria are definitely living things. They reproduce by dividing their cells. They need food, water, and oxygen to survive. Some can move around on their own.

Viruses can't do anything until they invade a living cell. Then they take over the cell. Viruses are completely parasitic [par·uh·**sit**·ik], which means that they can live and reproduce only inside the cells of other organisms. They are "living" in only one sense: they control their own reproduction. Outside a **host** cell, however, a virus is **inert**. It just sits and waits for a host to come along.

host (hohst)—a living thing on which another living thing lives

inert (in·**urt**)—having no power to move or act

Virus
- not-quite living particle
- must invade a cell to survive
- reproduces quickly inside a cell
- difficult to kill
- some viruses are killed by vaccines

Microorganism

Bacteria
- living organism
- can survive on its own
- reproduces by dividing its cells
- killed by antibiotics

How Cells Function

In order to understand why viruses are dangerous, you have to understand how they interact with cells. All cells—plant, animal, or bacteria—contain strands of chemicals called *RNA* and *DNA*. Roughly speaking, DNA is the cell's master recipe, and RNA is its chef. RNA "cooks" the DNA, eventually making the organism called for in the DNA recipe. Whenever RNA and DNA reproduce, their goal is to turn out perfect, unchanging copies of themselves.

Viruses are strands of RNA or DNA without a cell to do all the cooking that the complete recipe requires. That's why they need to invade cells. Once inside, the trouble begins. 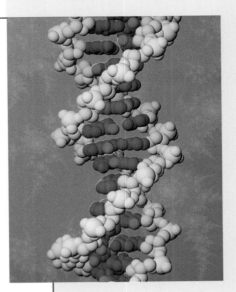 **②** *Strategy Alert!*

Invading a Cell

It might sound odd, but a virus uses its shape as a weapon to invade a cell. If a virus wants to invade a particular cell, it grows into a particular shape. For example, some viruses are thin rods. Some look like six-sided bullets. Others bristle with spikes. One even looks like a spider with a doll's head!

Cells defend themselves by trying to stay cut off from the outside world. But cells still need entryways through their **membranes** so that **nutrients,** salts, and other needed materials can enter. Cells also need openings to throw out waste products. These areas are called *receptor sites*, and they are shaped differently on different cells. Viruses try to find receptor sites through which they can fit.

If a virus finds an opening in a cell that is a good fit, it can "fool" the cell into letting it in. Once inside, the virus's DNA interferes with the cell's DNA "cooking" process, although no one knows exactly how.

DNA

Stop and Ask **②**

If it doesn't make sense, what can I do? Scan to find clarifying information.

I didn't understand how a virus gets in a cell. I scanned the section and found that the virus looks for an opening in the cell that it can fit through. Then it fools the cell into letting it in.

membranes
(**mem**·braynz)—thin layers of tissue that cover or line certain organs

nutrients
(**noo**·tree·uhnts)—foods

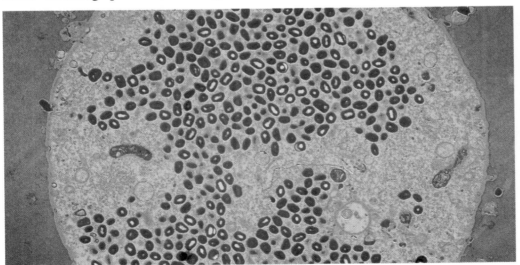

Viruses inside a cell

A Master Multiplier

The DNA in a virus uses a cell's DNA to produce copies of itself. This can happen very quickly. One doll's head virus can create about 100 new viruses, per cell, in about 30 minutes.

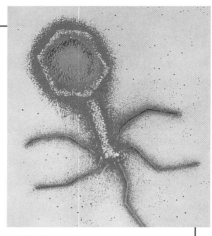

Doll's head virus

Those 100 viruses then leave that cell and invade 100 new cells. Once they reproduce, there can be 10,000 viruses. Then those 10,000 invade 10,000 more cells. Within a couple of hours, one virus can become 100 million viruses.

One thing that helps viruses stay ahead of the body's defenses and ahead of modern medicine is their rapid **evolution**. They can change their shape frequently in a process called *mutation*. Whenever a virus copies its DNA inside a cell, pieces of the DNA often get copied in the wrong order—just as you may sometimes mix up the position of the letters on your computer keyboard and type a word incorrectly. Because viruses change almost constantly, it is easy for them to find new ways to invade host cells and spread themselves around.

evolution
(ev·uh·loo·shuhn)—
process in which change
takes place

Deadly Outbreaks of the Past

The changing nature of viruses is best shown by one of the most common viral diseases, influenza, or simply "the flu." The flu has probably been attacking humans for at least 2,000 years. A deadly epidemic in Athens, Greece, in the year 430 B.C. may have been influenza.

Some writers in the Middle Ages clearly describe influenza epidemics. More recently, an outbreak of Spanish flu, which occurred between 1918 and 1919, killed about 22 million people worldwide. That's more than twice as many as the death toll from World War I. There were major flu epidemics in 1957 (Asian flu), in 1968 (Hong Kong flu), and in 1977 (Russian flu). In fact, a flu pandemic—a worldwide spreading of the disease—seems to occur about every ten years.

An influenza virus often breeds first in ducks or pigs somewhere in Asia. Then it sweeps across Africa and Europe, finally ending up in America. Why this pattern occurs is unclear. It might be because contact among humans, ducks, and pigs is more frequent in Asia.

In 1918, people wore masks. They mistakenly thought they would be protected from the flu.

How to Fight a Virus

It is difficult to kill a virus once it takes hold. Diseases caused by bacteria can be stopped by antibiotics. Because viruses work from inside cells, medicines can't attack viruses without attacking and killing the cells, too. A different plan is needed.

When viruses first move from one kind of animal to another, some of the more dangerous strains are weakened. Scientists use these weakened viruses to make **vaccines**. Vaccination allows the body to build up an immunity to the virus. If the virus tries to infect a body that has been vaccinated, the body's own defenses can kill it. Smallpox has been completely eliminated in humans, thanks to vaccination. The last known cases of smallpox were seen in 1977.

Viruses and Vectors

Vaccination doesn't work as well with influenza, however. The first year a person gets a flu shot, he or she probably won't get sick. But the next year, the same vaccine might not work as well. By the third year, there's a chance the vaccine won't work at all. The reason: the flu virus changes its form all the time. ⑦ *Strategy Alert!*

Viruses use another tool, called a *vector*, to keep infecting new host animals. Vectors are organisms that carry a virus from one host to another. In the case of the most deadly viruses, vectors allow the virus to spread before the host animal dies. This is important for the virus's survival. If the host dies before the virus is spread, the virus dies with it.

Vectors spread disease in two ways. The first is a set of **symptoms** caused by the virus. Symptoms in the host help it spread easily to other hosts before the original one dies. In the case of rabies, symptoms include frothing at the mouth and biting. The virus is spread by the infected animal's saliva. The same process is used by the cold virus in humans, which is spread by coughing and sneezing.

The second type of vector is an animal that carries the virus without getting sick from it. This is how mosquitoes spread viral diseases such as yellow fever.

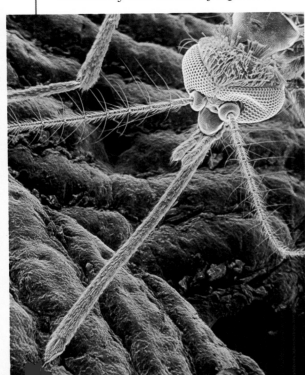

Mosquitoes like this one (shown in a magnified view) spread yellow fever and other diseases.

vaccines (vak•**seenz**)— substances used for the prevention of diseases

Stop and Ask ⑦

If it doesn't make sense, what can I do? Scan to find clarifying information.

I didn't understand what vectors are. What do they have to do with viruses? I scanned the section and found that a vector is an organism that carries a virus and helps it spread.

symptoms (**sim**•tuhmz)—signs of a disease

A Changing Battleground

Because there are so many viruses, and because they change rapidly, our fight against them takes place on a constantly changing battleground. New vaccines are needed all the time because new viruses appear frequently. AIDS is one of the newest. So far, no cure has been found for it.

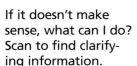 *Strategy Alert!*

Stop and Ask ?

If it doesn't make sense, what can I do? Scan to find clarifying information.

. . . .

This doesn't make sense. I don't remember how viruses change. I know if I scan back I can find that information. I can reread the section that explains that. I found the information on page 104.

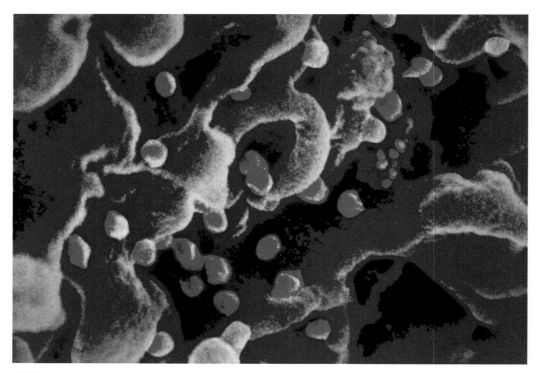

AIDS virus

Research has shown that viruses can even cause certain forms of cancer, such as adult T-cell **leukemia**. But little is known about this so far.

You might be familiar with the phrase "survival of the fittest." This means that the strongest creatures and plants survive. Most people see this fight for survival as a struggle among enemies: **predators** and **prey,** or one human battling another. Many biologists now believe, however, that one of the most important factors in how life has developed on Earth has been how organisms respond to viral infections. Fitness in the microscopic world may be more important than fitness in the visible world. Viruses have never given up the struggle. They continue to be one of our most dangerous enemies. And in many ways they remain an unsolved medical mystery.

leukemia
(loo·**kee**·mee·yuh)—a cancer of the blood

predators
(**pred**·uh·tuhrz)—living things that hunt other living things for food

prey (pray)—any animal hunted by other animals for food

Congratulations! You finished reading. Now read the habit and strategy for **After I Read**. Then read my notes below.

After I Read

Which **HABIT** will I learn?
Use what I've read.
If I develop this habit, I will think about how I can apply what I just read to my schoolwork and my life. This makes reading really useful.

Which **STRATEGY** will I use to learn this habit?
Decide what I want to know more about.

My Notes

- Strategy says I should decide what I want to know more about.

- I want to know more about the flu of 1918. I heard my grandmother say something about that.

- I've heard about yellow fever—and that picture of the mosquito is cool! I want to know more about how bugs spread disease.

- I've heard about DNA, but I don't know too much. That sounds interesting.

Now it's time to practice the three habits and strategies you learned when you read "Viruses: The Tiniest Killers." Start with **Before I Read**. Look at the box below. It should look familiar! Reread the habit you will practice. Reread the strategy you will use—then do it!

Before I Read

Which **HABIT** will I practice?
Decide what I need to know.
If I develop this habit, I will have a reason for reading. I will understand it better and remember more of what I read.

Which **STRATEGY** will I use to practice this habit?
Use graphic aids to ask purpose-setting questions.

Use the **Before I Read Strategy Sheet** for "Medical Detectives" (page 24 in your *Strategy Practice Book*) to decide what you need to know.

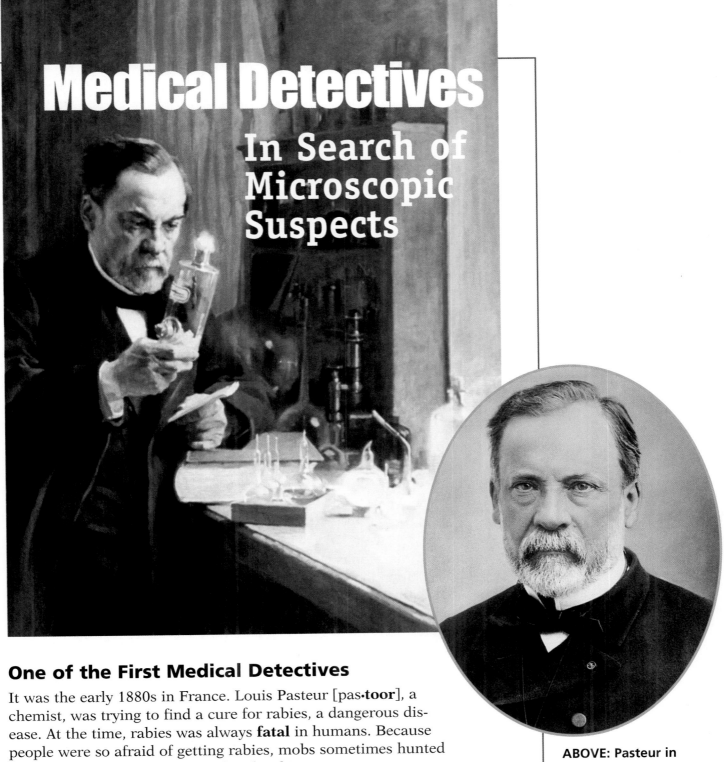

Medical Detectives
In Search of Microscopic Suspects

ABOVE: Pasteur in his laboratory

INSET: Louis Pasteur, 1889

fatal (**fayt·**l)—deadly

One of the First Medical Detectives

It was the early 1880s in France. Louis Pasteur [pas·**toor**], a chemist, was trying to find a cure for rabies, a dangerous disease. At the time, rabies was always **fatal** in humans. Because people were so afraid of getting rabies, mobs sometimes hunted down and killed people infected with rabies.

The symptoms of rabies are scary. First, you feel as though your skin is crawling. Then you become so excited that you can't calm down. You begin to feel very afraid. For some reason, you become afraid of water. Next, your body begins to shake wildly and you can't control it. In the next stage, you can't move at all. Then, death happens quickly.

Read the habit and strategy below. Look for the *Strategy Alerts!* as you continue to read.

While I Read

Which **HABIT** will I practice?
>**Stop and ask, "If it doesn't make sense, what can I do?"**
>If I develop this habit, I will stop and figure out what to do so what I'm reading makes sense. Then I can keep reading and not be lost.

Which **STRATEGY** will I use to practice this habit?
>Scan to find clarifying information.

 Use the **While I Read Strategy Sheet** for "Medical Detectives" (page 25 in your *Strategy Practice Book*) as you read.

Most often, rabies infects dogs and their relatives, such as wolves and foxes. It is also found in bats and raccoons. No matter which animal catches rabies, this dangerous disease produces the same results. Rabid animals die a painful death—so painful that it usually drives them mad. They will attack and bite anything that comes near them. In fact, that is how rabies usually is **transmitted**—through the bite of an infected animal. The virus that causes the disease lives in the animal's saliva. Pasteur tried to **isolate** the virus that causes the disease.

transmitted (trans·**mi**·tid)—passed from one to another

isolate (**ie**·suh·layt)—to separate from others

Finding the Virus

Whenever his friends heard of a rabid dog, they would send a telegram to Pasteur. The scientist then would send some of his assistants to catch the dog.

Once, two of Pasteur's assistants tied up a mad bulldog with a rope and held him down on a table. Pasteur put a glass straw in his own mouth. He moved close to the bulldog and sucked the dog's foaming saliva from its lips. Pasteur's action was either brave or foolhardy. One slip would have meant a fatal dog bite to his face.

Despite his efforts, Pasteur never found the virus that causes rabies. That's because viruses are extremely tiny organisms. They could not be seen by the best microscopes Pasteur had in his lifetime. The rabies virus wasn't found until 1903, nearly 20 years later.

Fighting the Unseen Organism

Even though Pasteur couldn't find the rabies virus, he developed a vaccine that would cure the disease. He did it by using a clever plan. He **deliberately** infected rabbits with saliva from mad dogs. He used rabbits because they usually don't carry rabies. Any animal that doesn't carry a disease probably has a way of killing it within its body.

First, Pasteur **euthanized** the rabbits. Then he cut out and crushed parts of their spinal cords—the thick cord of nerve tissue inside the backbone. The crushed rabbit spinal cords were aged, which weakened the virus. The aging took from one day to two weeks. The longer the aging period, the weaker the virus.

Pasteur then vaccinated a healthy dog with the rabbit tissue. That is, he injected the tissue into the animal's brain. He did this once a day for 14 days in a row. He used the oldest spinal tissue first. Each day, the virus that he used had been aged a little less. Finally, he put the vaccinated dog into a cage with a rabid dog. After a few days, he removed the "healthy" dog from the cage. It had been attacked and bitten by the rabid dog, but it showed no sign of rabies. Pasteur continued to test the dog for a year. When it failed to develop rabies, he knew he had found an effective vaccine against the disease. ② *Strategy Alert!*

deliberately
(di·**lib**·uhr·it·lee)—on purpose

euthanized
(**yoo**·thuh·niezd)—put to death in a painless way

If it doesn't make sense, what can I do? Scan to find clarifying information.

Pasteur with his rabbits in his laboratory, around 1884

The First Human Test

One healthy dog was no guarantee that Pasteur's rabies vaccine would work on humans. He needed to test his medicine on a person. That happened on July 4, 1885, the day that nine-year-old Joseph Meister was bitten by a rabid dog.

Meister was walking to school when the dog knocked him down and bit him again and again. The boy covered his face with his hands. A bricklayer who was walking by saw the attack and beat the dog off with an iron bar. Another neighbor brought out his gun and shot the dog.

Meister's parents took the boy to Pasteur in Paris. The youngster was so stiff from his many wounds that he could hardly walk. Meister would certainly die if he went untreated. Pasteur decided to try his vaccine on the boy.

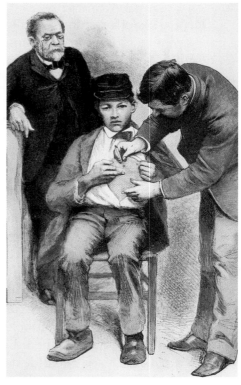

Louis Pasteur watched as nine-year-old Joseph Meister received the rabies vaccine in his stomach.

An "Old Softy"

Because Pasteur used and often killed animals in his experiments, a lot of people thought he must be a cruel man. In reality, however, he was an "old softy." Although he knew his work was necessary, he hated what he had to do to the test animals. He couldn't even assist in many of the operations that were required to perform the experiments.

Likewise, when Pasteur began trying his vaccine on Joseph Meister, he grew very **anxious**. He was unable to work and he couldn't sleep. He even had a nightmare in which he saw young Joseph suffocating in his own saliva.

Joseph Meister received 12 shots in 11 days. The last one contained rabies vaccine that had been aged for only one day. The virus in it was still strong enough to kill. But young Joseph trusted Pasteur. That night, he said, "Dear **Monsieur** Pasteur, kiss me good night." The sick boy slept very well. Pasteur hardly slept at all.

Joseph Meister's doctor kept him under observation for ten more days. **Eventually** he sent him home, completely cured. The news brought many people to Pasteur's laboratory. They were seeking cures to other diseases. But Louis Pasteur was a chemist, not a physician. His assistants had to explain, "He does not cure individuals. He only tries to cure humanity."

anxious (ank·shuhs)—worried

Monsieur (muh·syur)—the French word for *Mr.*

eventually (i·ven·choo·uhl·ee)—after some time

The Work of the CDC

Louis Pasteur was one of the first modern medical detectives who track down invisible killers, such as rabies. Today, many of these detectives work in Atlanta, Georgia, at America's "FBI of diseases"—the Centers for Disease Control and Prevention (CDC). The agency works both in the United States and around the world.

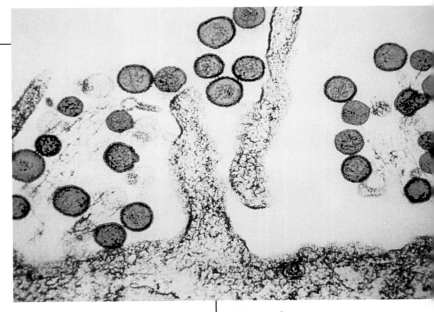

The CDC has become famous since the outbreak of AIDS. Like rabies, this deadly disease is caused by a virus. It attacks the body's immune system, which defends the body against illness. AIDS can be spread in several ways. Most often, however, the virus is spread from infected people through sexual contact, drug use, or blood **transfusions**.

Today, AIDS is probably the best-known virus for which the CDC is seeking a cure. But there are others as well. Hantavirus is a deadly virus spread by mice. Hantavirus is found mostly in the southwestern United States. Dengue [**deng**·gay] fever is also caused by viruses. It is known as "breakbone fever" because it causes severe pain in the joints. The disease is reaching **epidemic** proportions in South and Central America. Some cases have been found in Texas. The CDC also tracks outbreaks of rabies and influenza, as well as diseases caused by bacteria.

Searching for Clues

When an outbreak of a disease occurs, CDC investigators first try to find out what the victims have been doing and what they might have in common. They collect information from the doctors who treated the victims. If possible, they also collect blood and tissue samples. Then, like detectives, they try to find a pattern: Did all these people eat at the same pizza parlor? Did they go to the same dog show? Did they buy ground beef from the same supermarket?

@ *Strategy Alert!*

Hantavirus

transfusions (tranz·**fyoo**·zhuhnz)— blood or blood products given through a vein

epidemic (ep·i·**dem**·ik)—rapid spreading of disease to many people at the same time

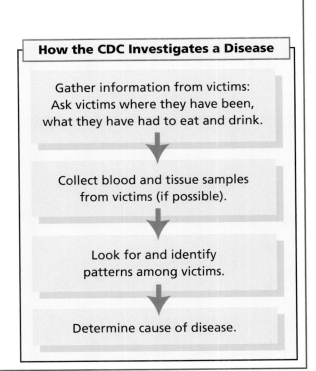

How the CDC Investigates a Disease

Gather information from victims: Ask victims where they have been, what they have had to eat and drink.

Collect blood and tissue samples from victims (if possible).

Look for and identify patterns among victims.

Determine cause of disease.

Stop and Ask ?

If it doesn't make sense, what can I do? Scan to find clarifying information.

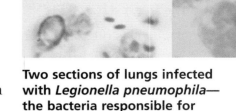

An Unusual Outbreak

CDC scientists tracked down a new disease in a hotel in Philadelphia, Pennsylvania, in 1976. There, at a meeting of a group called the American Legion, more than 150 people had become ill. Twenty-nine of them died.

Two sections of lungs infected with *Legionella pneumophila*— the bacteria responsible for 29 deaths in 1976

Stories began appearing about possible causes of the disease, which is now known as "Legionnaires' disease." For example, some people thought that the victims had been poisoned. Others believed that the people had caught the flu. One person even said that the illnesses were caused by visitors from outer space!

culprit (**kul**·prit)— person or thing that is guilty

The real answer was pretty dull, but very dangerous. The **culprit** was a strain (or particular type) of bacteria. It eventually was given the scientific name *Legionella pneumophila* [noo·moh·**feel**·uh]. The bacteria were found to be growing in the hotel's air conditioning system. Once the bacteria had been identified, the disease could be controlled by antibiotics.

A Deadly Strain

Stop and Ask ❓

If it doesn't make sense, what can I do? Scan to find clarifying information.

In 1995, a laboratory worker died in the town of Kikwit, Zaire [zie·**eer**], in central Africa. (Today Zaire is known as the Democratic Republic of the Congo.) He had undergone two operations, but doctors believed his death was caused by a virus. Many of the people who had assisted at the operations also became ill.

Blood samples of 14 of the sickest people were sent to the CDC. The agency discovered that they all were infected with the Ebola virus. The Ebola strain acts very quickly. It kills by turning the internal organs into liquid. This causes severe bleeding. Victims of Ebola can die within a few days. ❓ *Strategy Alert!*

Ebola virus

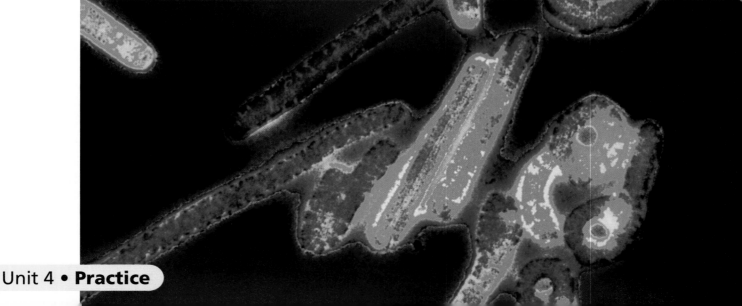

Cities in Quarantine

Back in Zaire, the government completely closed off Kikwit, a city of half a million people. Armed guards were stationed at checkpoints around the city to turn away visitors. Kinshasa, Zaire's capital, a city of five million people, also was closed. When the outbreak in Kikwit was over, about 250 people had died from Ebola.

Even though there is no cure for Ebola, there are ways to fight it. The virus has a very short **incubation** period—about 4 to 16 days. The disease is most easily transmitted during this period. So someone who has it cannot infect other people for very long. The way to fight Ebola is to isolate its victims until the incubation period is over. Also, Ebola is not easy to transmit. Usually a person has to come into direct contact with infected blood or body fluids in order to catch the virus.

Manhattan Mystery

In the summer of 1999, the CDC investigated two strange disease outbreaks in New York City. One outbreak affected people; the other involved animals.

Outside the city, on Long Island, 23 horses had a disease that was unknown to local veterinarians. Nine of the horses died. Mysteriously, hundreds of wild crows were dying as well.

Meanwhile, back in Manhattan, 60 people became ill with encephalitis [en·sef·uh·**lie**·tis], a virus that causes swelling of the brain. Seven eventually died. Could there be a connection among all the animal and human victims?

After Labor Day weekend, Dr. Tracey McNamara, the Bronx Zoo's **pathologist,** started getting calls about the dead crows around the city. Dead crows also were turning up on the zoo grounds. At the same time, McNamara noticed that some of the zoo's birds were ill. One bald eagle was shaking. A **cormorant** spent his last hours before he died swimming in circles. A Chilean [chil·**ay**·uhn] flamingo and snowy owl also died. Dr. McNamara wondered if the illnesses affecting the birds and the people were the same. At first, no one believed her. "If I had a nickel for every person who told me I was nuts, I'd retire," she said later. ⑦ *Strategy Alert!*

The snowy owl and the cormorant (below) were among the stricken animals.

incubation
(in·kyuh·**bay**·shuhn)—period of time between infection and onset of symptoms

pathologist
(pa·**thol**·uh·jist)—doctor who determines a cause of death

cormorant
(**kor**·muhr·uhnt)—a large sea bird

Stop and Ask ❓

If it doesn't make sense, what can I do? Scan to find clarifying information.

Some scientists thought the disease affecting people might be St. Louis encephalitis, a disease usually seen in more southern areas. This dangerous illness is spread by mosquitoes. But it had never affected birds before. The mystery deepened.

Two special laboratories, one in Ames, Iowa, and one in Fort Collins, Colorado, examined samples of dead bird tissue and samples of human tissue. Both labs confirmed what McNamara thought—the same disease was affecting the animals and the people. But it wasn't St. Louis encephalitis. The mysterious illness turned out to be West Nile virus. This virus had caused encephalitis in people and in horses in Africa, Australia, the Middle East, and Europe. Further tests showed that the people, horses, crows, and zoo birds in New York that had become sick in this outbreak had all caught the West Nile virus. That information solved the mystery, but not the problem.

Blame It on the Mosquito

The West Nile virus is spread by common mosquitoes. Entomologists (scientists who study insects) flew in helicopters over New York's neighborhoods. They sprayed mosquito breeding areas, such as abandoned tires or half-filled swimming pools, with pesticides. The city also distributed cans of bug repellent to combat the insect disease carriers. As predicted, when the mosquitoes died, the outbreak of the virus died, too.

Is the threat of these disease-carrying mosquitoes gone? Unfortunately, no. The story of the West Nile virus in New York has not ended. The virus has been identified in 23 species of animals. It has even turned up in tissues from a stray cat. In December 1999, New York City labs started to test bats and other animals. Scientists fear that when disease-free mosquitoes bite these infected animals, they will pick up enough virus to spread the disease again.

Cause and Cure of Some Diseases		
Disease	**Cause**	**Treatment/ Cure**
Rabies	Virus spread through the saliva of infected animals	Pasteur's vaccine
Ebola	Virus spread through infected blood or body fluids	No treatments No cure
AIDS	Virus spread through infected blood or body fluids	Antiviral drugs slow virus growth; No cure
Legionnaires' disease	Bacteria	Antibiotic drugs
West Nile virus	Virus spread through infected mosquitoes	No treatments No cure

The drama of the West Nile virus continues. So do similar stories around the globe. Luckily for us, most of these microscopic "suspects" are no match for the medical detectives at the CDC. Like Pasteur before them, these scientists and doctors will continue to track down the clues they need to solve medical mysteries.

 *Strategy Alert!*

Stop and Ask ?

If it doesn't make sense, what can I do? Scan to find clarifying information.

Now that you've finished reading, review the **After I Read** habit below. Think about what you read in "Medical Detectives" as you practice the strategy.

After I Read

Which **HABIT** will I practice?
Use what I've read.
If I develop this habit, I will think about how I can apply what I just read to my schoolwork and my life. This makes reading really useful.

Which **STRATEGY** will I use to practice this habit?
Decide what I want to know more about.

 Use the **After I Read Strategy Sheet** for "Medical Detectives" (page 26 in your *Strategy Practice Book*) to use what you've read.

Now read "Curing the Common Cold" and apply these three habits and strategies.

Before I Read

Which **HABIT** will I apply?
Decide what I need to know.

Which **STRATEGY** will I use to apply this habit?
Use graphic aids to ask purpose-setting questions.

While I Read

Which **HABIT** will I apply?
Stop and ask, "If it doesn't make sense, what can I do?"

Which **STRATEGY** will I use to apply this habit?
Scan to find clarifying information.

After I Read

Which **HABIT** will I apply?
Use what I've read.

Which **STRATEGY** will I use to apply this habit?
Decide what I want to know more about.

 Use the **Self-Assessment Sheet** for "Curing the Common Cold" (pages 27–28 in your *Strategy Practice Book*) as you read to see how well you can apply the habits and strategies.

Curing
the Common Cold

Think about colds. Most of us get at least two colds a year, and many of us get four. It's not unusual for young children to get as many as 12 colds every year! You may have wondered why there is no cure for the common cold. After all, medical researchers have found cures for more serious diseases. So why haven't they figured out the cold? Read on. The cold may be common, but it's not simple.

What Is a Common Cold?

Common colds cause sneezes, sore throats, and runny, stopped-up noses. Sometimes you get a cough; sometimes you have a slight fever. You feel tired, and your muscles usually ache. You might get a more serious **infection,** such as pneumonia [noo·**mohn**·yuh] or bronchitis [bron·**kie**·tis], after a cold because your body's resistance to infection is weak.

infection (in·**fek**·shuhn)— a disease caused by germs

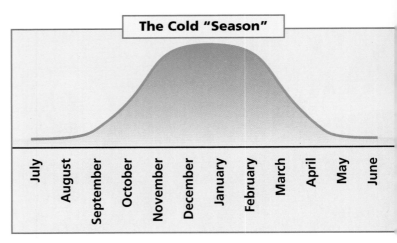

The Cold "Season"

July August September October November December January February March April May June

You can catch a cold any time of year. The cold "season" lasts from September to May. This chart shows the difference among the months.

Although colds are mild illnesses, they have a big impact on human lives. Millions of days of school or work are lost every year because of colds. Even if you go to school when you have a cold, you're probably not paying as much attention as you should be to what you're supposed to be doing.

We can catch a cold any time of the year, but we are more likely to catch a cold in the winter. This has nothing to do with cold temperatures, except that the air is drier when it is cold outside and moisture in the air helps protect the lining of our noses. Being cold doesn't give us a cold. In fact, trying to stay warm may help make us sick. We are more likely to stay indoors when it is cold outside. So we are exposed to more cold germs in the enclosed space of the house.

What Causes a Cold?

Colds are caused by viruses, tiny organisms that can't live on their own. They survive only in the living cells of another living creature. We "catch" a cold by breathing in a cold virus that someone has coughed or sneezed into the air or by getting a virus on our hands and then touching our eyes, nose, or mouth. A cold virus can't live long on its own—up to three hours outside someone's body. When a cold virus enters a living cell, it uses the cell's energy to grow. The virus reproduces itself and enters other living cells. The host cell is destroyed. This process eventually produces a disease, such as a cold.

When you have a cold, your body may be home to as many as 10,000 cold viruses! You probably have about 1,000 viruses when you first start to feel a cold coming on. Unlike bacteria, viruses do not respond to medicines such as penicillin, which can quickly knock out a bacterial infection. The medicines that many people take for a cold only help the cold symptoms—the stopped-up nose, achy muscles, and cough. They don't kill the viruses.

Our Valuable Immune System

Our bodies have an **efficient** system for fighting diseases. That immune system includes cells, tissues, and organs that work together to fight the germs—bacteria or virus—that make us sick. Blood vessels, skin, tears, even the hairs in your nose are all part of your immune system. Blood vessels carry **antibodies** and white blood cells that fight disease. Skin keeps many harmful germs from entering your body. Tears keep germs from entering through your eyes. Throat cells collect germs that sneak through your mouth. This immune system is a powerful force. The aches and fever that are part of a cold are signs that the immune system is working.

The immune system is specialized. Specific cells do specific jobs. Some cells recognize organisms or substances that don't belong in the body. Others mark the invaders, while still other kinds of cells prepare for the actual attack. The immune system attacks in two ways. To fight some kinds of infections, it makes antibodies. These special proteins are carried by the blood and destroy invading germs. To fight viruses, the immune system sends out killer T cells, which attack and kill the cells in which the viruses live. Remember, viruses cannot live on their own; they live in other cells. By killing the host cells, the T cells destroy the virus.

As amazing as this is, the immune system is even smarter. It has a memory. The immune system recognizes germs it has met before, so when the immune system meets them again, it kicks into action faster. You don't get as sick or you don't get sick at all. This is why vaccines work. When you receive an **immunization** for a disease such as measles, you get a weak dose of the disease. Your immune system revs up to take care of the invading viruses. The dose is big enough to teach your immune system what this disease's viruses are like. It's small enough so that you don't get really sick.

But what about curing the cold?

The Immune System

- Adenoids
- Lymph Glands
- Tonsils
- Thymus
- Blood Vessels
- Spleen
- Appendix
- Lymph Vessels
- Bone Marrow

The parts of your immune system work together to help your body fight diseases.

efficient (i·**fish**·uhnt)— getting results with the least possible effort or waste

antibodies (**an**·ti·bod·eez)—disease-fighting organisms

immunization (im·yuh·ni·**zay**·shun)— treatment to make a person resistant to a disease

Can We Cure the Common Cold?

If the immune system remembers diseases, why do we keep getting colds? If scientists can make vaccines, why haven't they developed a cold vaccine?

A cold virus is complex. One scientist made an exact model of a cold virus. His creation looked like a miniature planet, filled with mountain peaks and deep canyons. There are more than 200 different cold viruses that belong to five viral families. The immune system must treat each virus as something new. Learning about one cold virus doesn't help your body defend itself against another. To complicate matters, these viruses keep changing. This makes it hard for the immune system to recognize and fight them. That's why we keep catching colds.

Because a vaccine is developed to help the immune system fight a disease, these same conditions apply. One vaccine works only on one virus that is formed a particular way. This has made it impossible for scientists to develop a vaccine for the common cold.

Testing Cold-Cure Drugs

Testing the effectiveness of new cold drugs is tricky. With most drugs, scientists first run laboratory tests. They test the drug on animals, usually rats and mice. They infect the animal with the disease, then give the drug to the animal to see if it works. These animal tests also help scientists observe the drug's **side effects**.

side effects—unwanted reactions to drugs

However, the cold viruses that bother humans do not give rats and mice a cold. Scientists have been able to infect chimpanzees with cold viruses, but the chimps don't get sick. This means that after running laboratory tests, scientists must test new drugs on humans. Because of the possibility of side effects, they don't usually test a drug on people without first testing it on animals. The exception would be a drug to treat an unusual or dangerous disease—certainly not the common cold!

Mice do not get sick from human cold viruses.

A Cold Spray

In the late 1990s, scientists developed a spray that helps ward off cold viruses. In test cases, people who were exposed to colds and used the spray didn't get as sick as people who didn't use the spray. Some people using the spray didn't catch the cold at all. This spray isn't something you spray in the air to kill cold viruses. It's a spray to use in your nose.

To understand how the spray works, you need to know two things. First, one family of cold viruses is the rhinovirus. This is a big family and accounts for more than 40 percent of the colds we get—more than any other family. This group attacks your **respiratory** system. Most rhinoviruses enter your body through your nose. (The word part *rhino* actually means "nose.")

The second thing to know is that the cells in our bodies are coated with special molecules that sit on the outside of a cell and act as a sort of glue. They help substances stick to each other. They also help cells stick to each other. The cells in the lining of your nose are covered with a coating called *ICAM-1*. When you breathe in a rhinovirus, it grabs onto a cell coated with ICAM-1 and gets an easy ride into a cell.

respiratory
(**res**·puh·ruh·taw·ree)—
having to do with
breathing

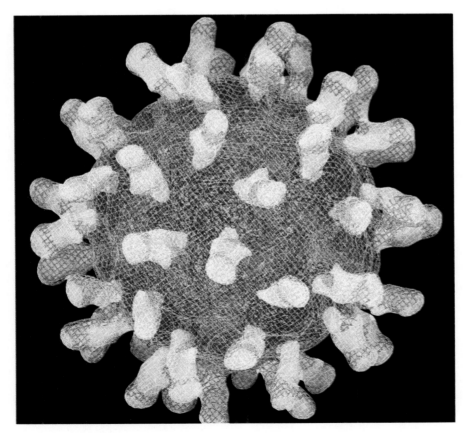

Reconstruction of a human rhinovirus attached to ICAM-1 receptors. The virus is the sphere, and the ICAM-1 receptors are the cylinders.

attracted (uh·**trak**·tid)—
drawn to

Now you probably remember that scientists have been frustrated by the changing nature of cold viruses. If the form of these viruses keeps changing, would the virus keep being **attracted** to an ICAM-1? Yes. Although the shape of cold viruses changes, the point at which a cold virus attaches to an ICAM-1 stays the same. Discovering that helped scientists develop the nasal spray.

Here's how the spray works. The mist in the spray contains lots of fake ICAM-1s. When you use the spray, you fill your nose with these fakes. The cold viruses don't seem to know the difference, so many of them latch onto the fakes. The viruses that grab a fake ICAM-1 can't get to a cell in your body. The virus dies, and the cold goes away.

Developing Other Cold Cures

This spray is just one possible cold treatment. Even though it seems to work, it will be a long time before it becomes available. Drug companies need to figure out when people should begin to take the spray, how often they can use it, and how much of it they should take at a time. In the meantime, scientists are experimenting with substances that will protect the ICAM-1s from the cold viruses. One substance they developed works by disconnecting cold viruses and ICAM-1s that had already become attached. Another is interferon [in·tuhr·**feer**·on], a substance the body naturally makes to fight disease. Scientists can now make interferon in a laboratory.

preventative
(pri·**ven**·tuh·tiv)—able to keep from happening

Research for the cure of other diseases may help cure the common cold. Cures or **preventative** drugs for AIDS are very important in the medical-research world. AIDS, a severe disorder, is caused by a virus that weakens the immune system. Scientists involved in AIDS research are learning a great deal about the immune system. Their work helps scientists who are researching cures for other viral diseases, including the common cold.

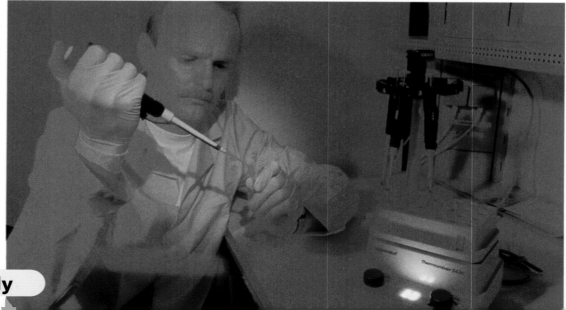

This scientist is involved in research to cure AIDS.

What Does All This Mean?

Because there are five different cold virus families and hundreds of different viruses, it will probably be a long time before there is a ready cure for the common cold. So what do we do? What we can do is try hard not to get a cold in the first place. If we do get one, we need to take care of ourselves so that we get better faster.

Avoiding a cold may be easier than you think. Wash your hands often. Keep them away from your nose, mouth, and eyes. Eat a balanced diet that includes many fruits and vegetables, and drink at least eight glasses of water a day. Try to get a good night's sleep every night. Exercise regularly, and spend time with people you like. All these things help keep your immune system strong. These tips are common sense, and you've heard them all before. The key is to really follow them!

Colds may be bothersome, but they aren't necessarily bad. You'll get a cold two or three days after you've been exposed to the cold virus. Most colds last a week, but the cough might last a week or longer. When you do get a cold, use common sense. Get plenty of rest, and drink warm, soothing liquids. Cover your mouth with a tissue when you cough or sneeze. Throw used tissues away immediately and wash your hands often, so that you don't infect other people. If you spend time with young children who are not yet in school, you may have a hard time avoiding getting colds. Young children get a lot of colds because their immune systems haven't learned how to fight the cold viruses.

So, the next time you get a cold, sit back and relax. Take care of yourself and your cold. Just think: this is one cold you'll never have again.

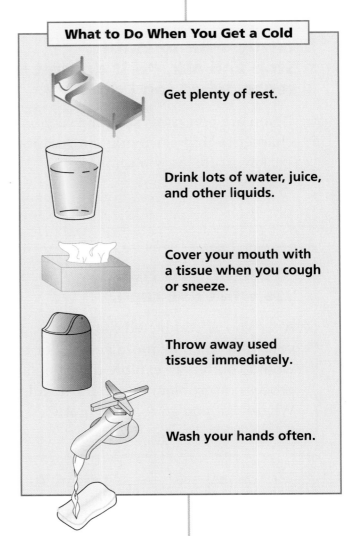

What to Do When You Get a Cold

Get plenty of rest.

Drink lots of water, juice, and other liquids.

Cover your mouth with a tissue when you cough or sneeze.

Throw away used tissues immediately.

Wash your hands often.

Put Your Habits to Work in

Literature	Social Studies	Science	Math

Before I Read Habit:
Decide what I need to know.

Before you read a chapter or section in your math book, use the graphic aids in the chapter to figure out what you need to know. Then ask purpose-setting questions to guide your reading.

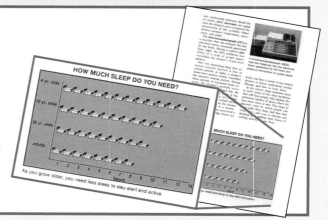

While I Read Habit:
Stop and ask, "If it doesn't make sense, what can I do?"

If you are confused, scan the section or chapter to find clarifying information. Look for key words as you scan.

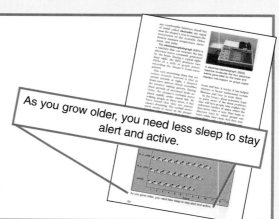

As you grow older, you need less sleep to stay alert and active.

After I Read Habit:
Use what I've read.

After you've completed the chapter, decide what you want to know more about. For example, would you like to explore a particular process or problem in greater detail? Where can you go to learn more?

I want to know more about …

You may wish to use the **Put Your Habits to Work Sheet** (page 29 in your *Strategy Practice Book*) to practice these habits in your other reading.

Unit 5
Endangered or Extinct?
Theme: Animals

In this unit, you will develop these 3 habits for all readers.

Before I Read Habit:
Check it out!

While I Read Habit:
Stop and ask, "Does it make sense?"

After I Read Habit:
React to what I've read.

Learn 3 of the 9 Habits

In this unit, you will develop three habits—one for before you read, one for while you are reading, and one for after you finish reading. Start with **Before I Read**. Read the habit and strategy. Then read my notes below.

Before I Read

Which **HABIT** will I learn?
> **Check it out!**
> If I develop this habit, I can find out something about what I am going to read so that I know what to expect.

Which **STRATEGY** will I use to learn this habit?
> Decide what the internal organization of the selection is.

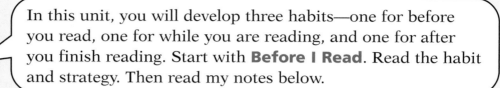

My Notes

- Strategy says to decide what the internal organization of the selection is. That means to see how the article is set up.

- The title and introduction tell me that the selection must be about endangered and extinct animals.

- I see the word "causes" in several headings. Cause and effect is one way to organize ideas. Maybe this selection has a cause-and-effect organization.

Going, Going, Gone

Hua Mei, the first surviving giant panda born in a North American zoo

Introduction

In the 1500s sailors found a huge, clumsy, flightless bird on the Mauritius [mor·**ish**·uhs] Islands in the Indian Ocean. The dodo couldn't move very fast and it couldn't fly. Animals that the sailors brought with them hunted and killed the dodos. Whenever the sailors wanted food they clubbed the birds. By 1680 the dodos became **extinct**.

In August of 1999, the birth of Hua Mei [hwah may] at the San Diego Zoo was reason for celebration around the world. Why all the excitement? Scientists believe there are just 1,000 giant pandas left in the wild and about 120 in captivity. Bamboo, the sole food of giant pandas in the wild, is scarce. The destruction of the bamboo forests in China has caused the near-extinction of the giant panda. Without **intervention,** the only giant pandas left will be those born in zoos.

A model of the extinct dodo

extinct (ik·**stingkt**)— no longer living

intervention (in·tuhr·**ven**·shuhn)—the act of coming in to help

Now read the habit and strategy for **While I Read**. When you see ❓, read my notes in the margin.

While I Read

Which **HABIT** will I learn?
> **Stop and ask, "Does it make sense?"**
> If I develop this habit, I will stop now and then to make sure I understand what I'm reading.

Which **STRATEGY** will I use to learn this habit?
> Identify the causes of events.

species (**spee**·sheez)— a group of living things that are alike in certain ways

paleontologists (pay·lee·uhn·**tol**·uh·jists) —scientists who study ancient forms of life, such as fossils

fossil (**fos**·uhl)— the hardened remains of a plant or animal

amoebae (uh·**mee**·bee)— tiny organisms that change form

What Is Extinction?

Plants and animals on our planet have become extinct since the earth began. Some scientists believe that extinction is a natural process. As one **species** disappears, another replaces it. This development takes place over millions of years. It creates a natural biological variety of living things. For all the species that we know today, there are thousands of others that lived millions of years ago. These extinct species are all gone. Archaeologists and **paleontologists** know this because they study the **fossil** record of plants and animals. When a fossil no longer appears, the scientists assume this species became extinct.

No extinct animal or plant has ever reappeared. During the history of the earth, masses of animals and plants have become extinct within a short period of time. These mass extinctions have happened five times. Today we are in the sixth period of mass extinction. What caused this to happen in the past? Why is it happening today?

Ecosystems

All living things, plants or animals, depend on other living things to stay alive. Every living thing from one-celled **amoebae** to giant dinosaurs is part of an ecosystem (a group of living things in an environment). Over millions of years, living things adapt to their environment and become part of ecosystems. When something disrupts the ecosystem, the living thing does one of two things: it adapts or becomes extinct. When one animal or plant dies, others that depend on it for food can die, too. When the ecosystem is disrupted, this leads to the extinction of some species within it.

Keystone Species

Creatures with the greatest impact on others in an ecosystem are called *keystone species*. The alligator, once an endangered species in the United States, is a keystone species in its swamp ecosystem. Alligators dig holes to rest and to stay cool. These fill with water and become small ponds. Plants and marine animals begin to inhabit the ponds. The alligator makes a nest of sticks and mud which soon becomes an island where plants and trees grow. Birds nest in the trees. When the alligator was hunted to near extinction, its ecosystem was almost destroyed. Without the alligators, there were no ponds and islands. No ponds and islands meant loss of **habitat** for other creatures. *Strategy Alert!*

Causes of Five Periods of Mass Extinction

Throughout history the loss of keystone species and ecosystems led to the gradual extinction of many species. But there were also periods of mass extinction when thousands of plants and animals disappeared quickly from the earth. Until 1600 A.D., major changes in the **geology** and climate of the earth caused major changes in the environment.

The earth is not a quiet planet. It is always changing. Earthquakes show that the land is shifting. Glaciers [**glay**·shuhrz] are constantly moving all around the world. Floods and storms wash away forests and grasslands. Violent changes in the land, sea, or climate can cause a loss of ecosystems. Loss of ecosystems in turn causes habitats for plants and animals to vanish. As a result, many plants and animals became extinct.

An alligator in its habitat on Cumberland Island, Georgia

Part of this Alaskan glacier is breaking off and falling into the ocean.

invertebrates (in·**vur**·tuh·britz)—animals that have no backbone

asteroid (**as**·tuh·royd)—one of many small celestial bodies that orbit the sun

Mass extinctions happened during dramatic changes in the earth.

The Ordovician [or·duh·**vish**·uhn] extinction happened about 440 million years ago. Scientists think this was caused by a sudden cooling of the earth's surface. This resulted in widespread glaciation. Lands that had been tropical were covered with ice sheets and glaciers. This caused between 20 and 50 percent of the species on Earth to become extinct.

During the late Devonian period, about 360 million years ago, scientists believe the same thing happened. As the seas cooled, many fish and marine **invertebrates** died. About one fourth of all species became extinct.

Around 250 million years ago, the Permian extinction occurred.

During that period, half of all living things disappeared. Some scientists believe that the earth was hit by a large object from space. Others believe the same climatic changes as the two previous periods were responsible. However, this time there was a warming of the earth's surface.

Volcanic eruptions and **asteroid** impacts seem to have caused the Late Triassic [trie·**as**·ik] extinction. About one third of all plants and animals on Earth disappeared.

Dinosaurs survived the Triassic extinction. But during the late Cretaceous [kri·**tay**·shuhs] extinction, they too disappeared. There is evidence that this was caused by a huge impact. Scientists think that a comet hit the earth in Central America. Although only 15 percent of all the species disappeared during this event, the dinosaurs were one of them. *Strategy Alert!*

Causes of the Sixth Mass Extinction

The earth is now in a period called the Holocene [**hoh**·luh·seen]. This period began 65 million years ago. Gradual extinction has been taking place for all that time. In the past 400 years, however, a mass extinction seems to have been going on. Its cause is not a meteor, glaciation, change in sea level, or global cooling. Its cause is anthropogenic [an·thruh·puh·**jen**·ik]. That is, it has been caused by humans. Humans deliberately or inadvertently are causing other species to become extinct. People have destroyed habitats and polluted the globe. They have hunted and collected plants and animals. People have introduced non-native plants and animals to regions where they did not belong. All of these are contributing to the loss of ecosystems. *Strategy Alert!*

Modern Causes

In the past 50 years, people all over the world have become aware of what extinction means. By placing animals and plants on an endangered species list, people hope to save them from extinction. In the 1980s, species were becoming extinct at the rate of one a day, or 365 per year.

Stop and Ask ?

Does it make sense? Identify the causes of events.

I understand how changes in climate were caused by things like glaciers, impacts, and volcanic eruptions. The changes in climate caused the extinction of millions of animals and plants.

Stop and Ask ?

Does it make sense? Identify the causes of events.

Another mass extinction is being caused by people destroying ecosystems.

Some Endangered Animals Today

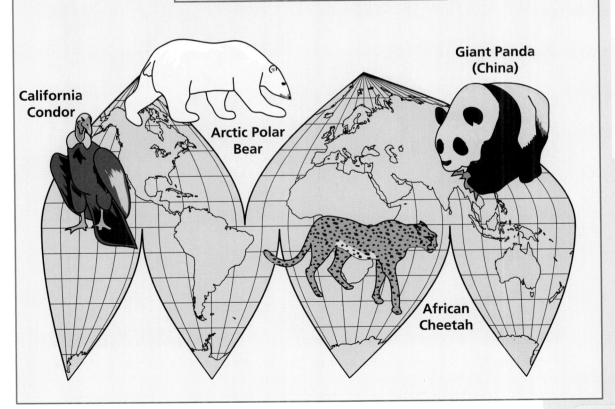

California Condor

Arctic Polar Bear

Giant Panda (China)

African Cheetah

Today it is 2.7 a day. That's about 1,000 per year! In the previous 600 million years, the rate was 10 per year. Animals that are near extinction include every species of whale, the African cheetah, the Arctic polar bear, and others. Plants, insects, and birds too numerous to list are endangered. In some parts of the world, one small plant of a species is all that survives. Why has this happened? There are many causes.

Expansion Causes Habitat Destruction

As the human population of the earth has grown, so has the need for farmland. More farms and people have led to destruction of many animals' and plants' natural habitats. As a result, ecosystems— the complex relationships of plants, animals, and their habitats—have also been destroyed.

One of the primary habitats being destroyed is the rain forest. In the Amazon region alone, more than one third of the rain forests has been destroyed. The habitat of hundreds of songbirds has gone with it. Several large **felines** are endangered. Removing the forest **canopy** and burning the land adds to the pollution of the atmosphere. In 1987 biologists counted 1,000 golden toads in the rain forest of Central America. Today they cannot find any. *Strategy Alert!*

Illegal logging of the rain forest near La Amistad Biosphere Reserve in Costa Rica

Another habitat being destroyed is the wetland. People build houses and roads right through wetlands. With the destruction of wetlands, habitats for small marine animals that are part of much larger ecosystems are disappearing. These include frogs, toads, salamanders, and many **microorganisms**. Birds that live in wetlands need to seek other places to nest. Animals that come to drink in marshy areas are deprived of water. With no place to hide, eat, or drink, an animal can soon disappear.

Pollution—Another Cause

As people build cities, houses, factories, and roads, the air is filled with smoke that is poisonous to plants and animals. People dump toxic chemicals in rivers. The chemicals are swallowed by fish and other marine creatures. Birds eat the fish and die. DDT, a pesticide used in the 1940s and 1950s, almost made several species of birds extinct. The bald eagle, whose egg shells were made too thin by DDT, almost disappeared in the 1960s. Since this bird was placed on the endangered species list, it has renewed itself. In 1999, the bald eagle was removed from the endangered species list.

Ecological disasters such as fires, oil spills, wars, and global warming—caused mostly by humans—are also causing many species to rapidly diminish.

The Effect of Hunting and Collecting

As people hunted animals for food, their fur, or to collect their exotic skins or feathers, they did not realize that these animals could disappear.

For example, in the early 1800s, there were so many passenger pigeons that flocks of them would block out the sun for as long as eight hours at a time. By 1914, these birds were extinct. One reason is that people hunted them because they were delicious to eat.

microorganisms (mie·kroh·**or**·guh·niz·uhmz)—tiniest living things

This bald eagle is no longer on the endangered species list.

Bison like these were brought back from the edge of extinction.

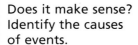

Stop and Ask ❓

Does it make sense?
Identify the causes
of events.

The events here
showed that
because people
hunted animals and
collected some
parts of animals,
the animals became
extinct. The passen-
ger pigeon became
extinct and the
bison almost did. It
makes sense that
some animals would
die out.

People killed many others because they thought the birds were pests.

Other animals have been over-hunted, too. In 1800, there were more than 60 million bison in the United States. By 1889, there were about 800. The bison had provided food, clothing, and shelter for the settlers as they moved west. No one believed bison could disappear. No one understood that they couldn't **reproduce** as fast as they were killed. When **conservationists** realized the danger of losing the last bison, people **intervened**. Today, there are about 260,000 bison in the United States. ❓ *Strategy Alert!*

Purple Loosestrife, a New England pest

Another Cause: Introduced Species

As people have traveled around the globe, they have brought animals and plants with them. Often these species are introduced to habitats that are not suitable for them. Sometimes the result is a loss of ecosystems for the native plants and animals.

In New England, people planted a flower called Purple Loosestrife. It grows quickly and looks very pretty, but it takes over the ponds and wetlands where it lives. Because it is killing off other plants, many native plant species are now disappearing.

During World War II a small snake whose native habitat was the Solomon Islands, New Guinea [**gi**·nee], and northern Australia was accidentally brought to the island of Guam. On Guam this tiny brown tree snake has eliminated several species of native lizards. It has destroyed most of the songbirds

The tiny brown tree snake has eliminated several species of lizards.

on the island, too. It is also threatening native bats. So far, no known means of destroying it have been found. Although nothing was done intentionally, this is a good example of what can happen when people introduce species into a new habitat. *Strategy Alert!*

Is there anything that can be done to stop the mass extinction happening today?

Can Laws Have an Effect?

In the United States the Endangered Species Act of 1973 makes it illegal to "kill, hunt, collect, harass, harm, pursue, shoot, trap, wound, or capture any endangered species." It prohibits buying and selling species that are endangered and protects **critical** habitat. Large fines and jail terms are given to those who break the law.

The Convention on International Trade in Endangered Species of Wild Fauna and Flora (CITES) is an international treaty that protects endangered species worldwide. It also bans buying and selling endangered species. However, not all nations obey this law. Whales are still hunted in some nations. Tigers, rhinoceros, elephants, and other unusual animals are still killed by **poachers** for their skins and ivory.

Stop and Ask ?

Does it make sense? Identify the causes of events.

• • • • • • • • • •

The cause of extinction here is people moving animals and plants into new habitats. The new animals kill the ones that are already there.

critical (**krit·i·**kuhl)— very important

poachers (**poh·**chuhrz)— people who hunt or fish illegally

These pilot whales have been hunted in the Faroe Islands.

The California condor

Stop and Ask

Does it make sense?
Identify the causes
of events.

· · · · · · · · · · ·

I understand that
people can also fix
problems they have
caused. Through
education and
efforts to protect
species, people can
cause some of
these extinctions to
stop.

Restoration of Species

Animals that are in danger of extinction are protected in the United States. In some instances they are **restored** in captivity and then released in the wild. In 1986 there were only two California condors left in the wild. These magnificent birds were victims of DDT. In the past 14 years, these birds have been bred and raised in captivity. Today they are being released in small numbers into the wild again.

Education

Much is being done throughout the world to educate people about the dangers of extinction. Efforts are being made to **curb** pollution, reduce **deforestation,** and limit or ban hunting. A worldwide effort is being made to save animals and plants. National parks, preserves, and conservation land are being saved to protect habitats. It is hoped that the tale of the dodo bird, passenger pigeon, and golden toad will not be repeated. Instead, stories of animals that have been saved—the California condor, the bison, and the giant panda—will be more common.

Humans have caused this latest mass extinction, and only humans can stop it. They can change how they treat the planet Earth and all its living things. (?) *Strategy Alert!*

Congratulations! You finished reading. Now read the habit and strategy for **After I Read**. Then read my notes below.

After I Read

Which **HABIT** will I learn?
React to what I've read.
If I develop this habit, I will take time to think about what I've just read. Deciding what I think and what I feel helps me remember it better.

Which **STRATEGY** will I use to learn this habit?
Decide whether a different set of circumstances would have caused a different conclusion.

My Notes

- Strategy says I should think about whether different circumstances would have made things turn out differently.

- I think that many things caused the first five extinction periods. If the meteorite hadn't hit the earth, maybe the dinosaurs would still be alive and we wouldn't be here.

- If we didn't do all the things we did to destroy habitats, there would probably not be any endangered animals now.

- And people are starting to show that if we change what we are doing, the result will be better for plants and animals.

Practice 3 of the 9 Habits

Now it's time to practice the three habits and strategies you learned when you read "Going, Going, Gone." Start with **Before I Read**. Look at the box below. It should look familiar! Reread the habit you will practice. Reread the strategy you will use—then do it!

Before I Read

Which **HABIT** will I practice?
Check it out!
If I develop this habit, I can find out something about what I am going to read so that I know what to expect.

Which **STRATEGY** will I use to practice this habit?
Decide what the internal organization of the selection is.

 Use the **Before I Read Strategy Sheet** for "Valuing 'Varmints'" (page 30 in your *Strategy Practice Book*) to find out something about what you're going to read.

Valuing "Varmints"

Martha, the last passenger pigeon

A prairie dog stands alert to danger.

Introduction

On September 2, 1914, a bird named Martha died at the zoo in Cincinnati, Ohio. At the time, Martha was the most famous bird in the world. The *New York Times* reported her death as one of its top stories. Why was Martha so important? Martha was the very last passenger pigeon in the whole world. Her death marked the end of her species. It also began a period in which other species have become extinct. Some species face the same fate even today.

In the Midwest, another animal may now be rushing toward the passenger pigeon's fate. Somewhere in the Great Plains, the last black-tailed prairie dog may soon be born. If so, prairie dogs will suffer the same end as passenger pigeons. Why did passenger pigeons disappear? Will those same causes affect prairie dogs?

Reread the habit and strategy below. Look for the *Strategy Alerts!* as you continue to read.

While I Read

Which **HABIT** will I practice?
> **Stop and ask, "Does it make sense?"**
> If I develop this habit, I will stop now and then to make sure I understand what I'm reading.

Which **STRATEGY** will I use to practice this habit?
> Identify the causes of events.

 Use the **While I Read Strategy Sheet** for "Valuing 'Varmints'" (page 31 in your *Strategy Practice Book*) as you read.

preyed (prayd)—killed, usually for food

A Large, Fast Bird

The passenger pigeon was a fairly large bird. It was bigger than other kinds of pigeons you may have seen. It was about 16 inches long. In sunlight, its shiny feathers reflected rainbow colors. The bird's long, thick tail feathers were mostly white. Two dark gray feathers sat in the middle of the tail. The bird's head was small, with bright orange eyes. It had a thin, black beak.

The bird was a fast flyer. John James Audubon, a bird expert, estimated that passenger pigeons could fly 60 miles an hour. This is about as fast as cars travel on highways. Other experts thought the birds could reach 100 miles an hour. One thing was certain: they were lightning quick in the air. They could turn or dive suddenly to escape from hawks, which **preyed** on them.

Numbers Beyond Imagination

When passenger pigeons weren't flying, they rested and slept in trees. This behavior is called *roosting*. The birds roosted in huge flocks. So many birds roosted in each tree that sometimes their weight caused branches to crash to the ground. And their droppings fell like snowflakes—only faster and messier!

The passenger pigeon was once probably the most **abundant** bird on Earth. Audubon reported that he

abundant (uh·**bun**·duhnt)— in plentiful supply

John James Audubon painted these passenger pigeons.

watched a flock of passenger pigeons fly past him for three solid days. "The air was literally filled with pigeons," Audubon wrote. The dark flock was so large that the birds blocked out the noontime sun.

Audubon thought that this flock had more than one billion birds. This is nearly four times the human population of the United States today! At about the same time, another bird-watcher watched a flock. He guessed that this flock was about 250 miles long. That is the distance between New York and Washington, D.C. That flock may have contained more than two billion birds! *Strategy Alert!*

Everyone who saw these flocks was amazed by their size. An English writer who saw the birds wrote home about them. When he went back to England, his readers accused him of making up stories! He had to **reassure** his readers that he was not **exaggerating**.

By the middle of the 1800s, about nine billion passenger pigeons may have lived east of the Mississippi River. At the time, there were only about six million people on the entire earth! In 1876, a Michigan flock covered an area 28 miles long and 3 miles wide. An even bigger flock was reported in Wisconsin. It was said to cover an area the size of New York City and Los Angeles combined! One Virginia man described them as "beyond number or imagination." This was only 38 years before Martha died.

Stop and Ask ?

Does it make sense? Identify the causes of events.

reassure
(ree·uh·**shoor**)—
to convince

exaggerating
(ig·**zaj**·uh·rayt·ing)—
making more of something than is true

What happened to all those birds in such a short time? No one knows for sure. When it happened, not many people studied the life cycles of animals. At the time, the science of ecology was unknown. Ecology is the science that studies the relationships between living things and their **environment**. It includes all the things that make an animal's life possible. Using what we know about endangered animals today, scientists can guess what happened. Most of the things that caused the passenger pigeon to become extinct can be linked to the actions of humans.

One Cause: Hunting

One factor that caused the pigeons' **demise** was hunting. Native Americans had hunted passenger pigeons for thousands of years. European settlers hunted them, too. The fatter the birds were, the better. Pigeon fat was used in cooking, and it was thought to be as sweet as butter. Pigeons were also fed to hogs, to fatten them up for **slaughter**. Besides being used as food, pigeons had other uses. Their fat was added to soap, and their feathers were used in blankets and pillows.  *Strategy Alert!*

People used many methods to catch and kill passenger pigeons. They shot the birds with rifles and handguns. They knocked them out of the air with sticks. They captured them in nets strung between trees. One trapper soaked grain in alcohol. When the birds ate it, they became drunk and could not fly. Then the trapper scooped them up. In some places, the birds were so thick in the trees that people could sneak up behind them, snatch them with their bare hands, and stuff them into sacks.

In the 1800s, hunters like these killed thousands of passenger pigeons.

environment (en·**vie**·ruhn·muhnt)—the conditions and surroundings in which something lives

demise (di·**miez**)—death

slaughter (**slaw**·tuhr)—the act of killing animals for market

Stop and Ask ?

Does it make sense? Identify the causes of events.

Many, many passenger pigeons were killed in these ways. In 1736, killed birds were so plentiful that they sold six for a penny. In 1874, some 25,000 pigeons a day were being taken from a single roosting in Michigan. Hunters killed another two million during the summer of 1878. By 1882, pigeons for the table were still selling for only thirty-five cents a dozen.

But by itself, even this large-scale hunting was not enough to destroy the species. Millions of birds were a small loss in a population of billions. Audubon saw another, much more serious danger. He wrote about it as early as 1830. He was convinced that only one thing could destroy the birds. That thing was the destruction of their habitat—the forests.

Another Cause: Lost Forests

Passenger pigeons ate all kinds of foods. They ate rice, grains, and seeds planted by farmers. But they preferred foods like acorns, fruits, berries, and beechnuts. Those foods were usually found in forests. The birds also made their nests and raised their young there. As long as nothing happened to America's forests, the pigeon population wasn't in danger.

But something did happen to the great American forests. They were chopped down to make way for farms. Until the end of the 1700s, passenger pigeons were plentiful in New England. They thrived along the northeast coast of the United States. Then more and more people came from Europe and settled in these areas. More of the forests were cleared; the pigeons were forced to move west to find food. Huge flocks still were reported in the Midwest—in Wisconsin, Illinois, Indiana, and Ohio. But the pigeons soon disappeared from the coast. *②* *Strategy Alert!*

The human population continued to grow. People kept cutting down forests to create farmland.

Stop and Ask

Does it make sense? Identify the causes of events.

Passenger pigeons preferred the acorns they could get from oak trees in forests like this.

Stop and Ask ❓

Does it make sense?
Identify the causes
of events.

The food supplies necessary
to feed the vast flocks **dwindled**.
At this point, hunting began to take
its toll. Some people knew that the
number of pigeons was **declining**.
They tried to take steps to prevent
the loss of the flocks. In the 1890s
and early 1900s, several states
passed laws to protect the birds.
The laws were not successful—
hunters still killed them.

Although Martha was the last
pigeon, the fate of her species was
sealed long before she died. The
pigeons needed huge flocks to survive. The flocks protected them
from **predators**. The flocks also
helped them find food, attract
mates, and raise their young. When
their numbers dropped below a
certain size, extinction became
certain. What that number was, no
one can say. Unfortunately, as the
pigeons moved west, pioneers
moved west, too. They hoped to
settle and farm there. This westward expansion added to the
pigeons' decline. It was a threat
to another animal species as well.
❓ *Strategy Alert!*

Dogs on the Prairie

American pioneers rolled westward
in their wagons during the 1800s.
They passed vast areas of prairie
dog towns. The prairie dog is not
really a dog. It is a rodent—a relative of rats and squirrels. It lives in
large colonies of burrows—or
tunnels—under the prairie. It
became known as a "prairie dog"
because of the dog-like barking
noises it makes.

A black-tailed prairie dog mother with
her pup

In 1804, explorer Meriwether
Lewis wrote in his journal that he
saw prairie dogs in "infinite numbers." There were five different
species of prairie dogs in the United
States. The most common one was
the black-tailed prairie dog. This
type lived over nearly half the land
area between the Mississippi River
and the Rocky Mountains.

Underground Colonies

No one knows how many prairie
dogs there were back then. Only
100 years ago, prairie dog towns
covered an area the size of Texas,
Oklahoma, and Arkansas. There
may have been more than five billion prairie dogs in all.

Prairie dogs aren't very large.
They are between 10 and 16 inches
long and weigh only one to three
pounds. Each member of a prairie
dog colony has a place in a family
group. The group is called a *coterie*
[**koh**·tuh·ree]. It usually consists of
one adult male, three or four adult
females, and several young. The
animals build an underground

burrow system. One system can be hundreds of feet long and 15 feet deep.

Prairie dogs post a **sentry** at each burrow opening. Sentries warn the colony about any approaching danger. Their yips and barks can be very loud. The different kinds of noises seem to mean different things. One researcher found that prairie dogs have different calls to warn of different predators. They have a distinct sound for hawks, coyotes, dogs, and humans. They may even be able to tell the difference between people of different sizes! As amazing as prairie dogs are, many people in the West think of them as "varmints," or pests.

Causes for Decline

Ranchers dislike the prairie dog because it eats grass. This grass is needed by cattle and horses for grazing. Prairie dogs also can spread **bubonic plague,** although only a few cases have been linked to the rodents in the last 50 years. Once a prairie dog town is set up, it can grow quickly. Many homeowners like watching the cute creatures from a distance. Homeowners become less happy when the rodents begin ruining lawns! Prairie dogs have been shot, poisoned, and buried alive as people have claimed the animals' towns.

Do the causes of the prairie dogs' decline match those that destroyed the pigeons? Some reasons are the same, but some are different. It is doubtful that hunting has had much impact on the total number of prairie dogs. More important has been poisoning and other methods of **extermination** that began early in the twentieth century. Even today, property owners will pay $1,000 a day to have the animals sucked out of their holes by huge vacuum trucks. Large numbers of prairie dogs have also been killed off by diseases. Today, only about 1.5 million acres of prairie dog towns remain—a tiny fraction of their former area. The U.S. Fish and Wildlife Service may list the black-tailed prairie dog as an endangered species. Why should anyone care about the decline of these "varmints"? (?) *Strategy Alert!*

A prairie dog guards a burrow at the National Wildlife Refuge in Oklahoma.

sentry (sen·tree)—one who stands guard

bubonic plague (boo·**bon·**ik playg)— a deadly, contagious disease, mostly spread by rats

extermination (ik·stur·muh·**nay·**shuhn) —killing

Stop and Ask ❓

Does it make sense? Identify the causes of events.

Prairie dogs near a fence stand watch by their burrow. Prairie dogs are very sociable.

activists (ak·tuh·vists)—people who work for a cause

relocated (ree·loh·kay·tid)—moved to a different place

Stop and Ask ?

Does it make sense? Identify the causes of events.

A Valuable Animal

Although unpopular, prairie dogs are important to the ecology of the plains. That's because as many as 170 other species depend on the animals. For example, prairie dogs are a major food source for hawks and other birds of prey. They also are eaten by coyotes, foxes, snakes, badgers, and the black-footed ferret, America's rarest mammal.

Ranchers and horseback riders don't like prairie dog towns because their animals often step in burrow entrances and are injured. Even the holes, however, are useful. They provide homes for burrowing owls, squirrels, snakes, salamanders, and insects. And the constant chewing of the grass by prairie dogs actually helps new grasses and plants grow, providing food for the many animals in the area.

A Last-Ditch Attempt?

People do care about the decline in the population of prairie dogs. Many have made efforts to protect the animals. The Cheyenne River Indian Reservation in South Dakota is protecting a 5,000-acre prairie dog town. Montana's Fort Belknap Reservation has nearly 14,000 acres of towns. In Colorado, **activists** have insisted that prairie dogs be **relocated** instead of killed before a construction project can begin on the site of a town. ? *Strategy Alert!*

In spite of these efforts, prairie dogs still are listed as varmints in every state where they are found. Killing the animals is actually encouraged. There are now about 50 million prairie dogs in America. Is that enough? No one can say for sure. No one can guarantee that the fate of the passenger pigeon will not be repeated.

Now that you've finished reading, review the **After I Read** habit below. Think about what you read in "Valuing 'Varmints'" as you practice the strategy.

After I Read

Which **HABIT** will I practice?
React to what I've read.
If I develop this habit, I will take time to think about what I've just read. Deciding what I think and what I feel helps me remember it better.

Which **STRATEGY** will I use to practice this habit?
Decide whether a different set of circumstances would have caused a different conclusion.

Use the **After I Read Strategy Sheet** for "Valuing 'Varmints'" (page 32 in your *Strategy Practice Book*) to react to what you've read.

Apply 3 of the 9 Habits

Now read "DDT and the Peregrine Falcon" and apply these three habits and strategies.

Before I Read

Which **HABIT** will I apply?
Check it out!

Which **STRATEGY** will I use to apply this habit?
Decide what the internal organization of the selection is.

While I Read

Which **HABIT** will I apply?
Stop and ask, "Does it make sense?"

Which **STRATEGY** will I use to apply this habit?
Identify the causes of events.

After I Read

Which **HABIT** will I apply?
React to what I've read.

Which **STRATEGY** will I use to apply this habit?
Decide whether a different set of circumstances would have caused a different conclusion.

 Use the **Self-Assessment Sheet** for "DDT and the Peregrine Falcon" (pages 33–34 in your *Strategy Practice Book*) as you read to see how well you can apply the habits and strategies.

DDT
and the
Peregrine Falcon

A peregrine falcon soars through the sky.

Peregrine [**per**·uh·grin] falcons are part of a large group of birds that includes hawks, eagles, and falcons. The peregrine received its name, which means "traveler," because some peregrines travel long distances in winter. Peregrines are found on every continent except Antarctica. Because they live and nest in high cliff areas, peregrines can survive well in many cities such as Philadelphia, Boston, and New York. There the tall, cliff-like buildings serve as fine nesting areas for peregrines.

In the early 1960s, however, bird lovers noticed that peregrines were disappearing. The number of young peregrines was getting smaller. What was the cause? People became concerned. Falcons, especially peregrines, have had a long and interesting relationship with human beings.

A hunting falcon wearing a hood

altitude (al·ti·tood)—
height

Crusades (kroo·saydz)
—religious wars fought
in the Middle Ages

A Look Back

Falcons have been trained for hunting for more than 4,000 years. No one knows for sure where the practice started. From historical records, though, we have learned that there were falconers, people who trained falcons, in many ancient countries, such as China, India, and Egypt. Peregrines are especially prized among falconers. Peregrine falcons have somewhat longer and more graceful wings than other falcons. They are considered beautiful and intelligent—for a bird, anyway!

At first sight, there's nothing unusual about the way the peregrine falcon "cruises" through the sky. When it spots its prey, however, look out! The peregrine doesn't simply swoop down upon its intended meal, as other birds do. Instead, it first flies up to a higher **altitude**. Then it folds its wings close to its body and begins a rocket-like dive toward its prey. In this position, the peregrine reaches speeds of up to 200 miles an hour—that's nearly as fast as an airplane! When swooping, or diving, the peregrine is the fastest animal on earth. Quite a feat of flying!

In the Middle Ages, English knights often took their favorite birds to church with them. In 1396, during the **Crusades,** the son of the Duke of Burgundy was captured by enemies. In order to have his son returned unharmed, the duke had to pay 12 white gyrfalcons. Nearly 24 inches in length, these are the largest of the falcons.

Falconry, the practice of training falcons for hunting, is still around today. Audiences are mesmerized by the birds' jet-like dives. The sport of falconry takes patience and dedication. The birds require much attention and training.

A fifteenth century hawking party

Falcons in Wartime

During World War II, the United States Army tried to use the peregrine's hunting ability to their advantage. At that time, the Germans used **homing pigeons** to carry messages. The U.S. Army wanted a way to catch the pigeons and read those messages. The plan was to train falcons to kill the German pigeons. This basic idea might have worked, but army planners tried to carry it further. They wanted the birds to attack paratroopers as they jumped out of planes. The idea was to train the falcons to cut parachutes. How could birds accomplish this? With knives attached to their chests!

The plan never went very far. Falcon experts worried that enemy soldiers would try to shoot the attacking falcons. In the end, the army acquired only three birds—a red-tailed hawk, an American kestrel (another very small falcon), and one peregrine.

Ironically, during World War II when the U.S. Army was considering using falcons to kill German pigeons, the English (**allies** of the United States) were actually killing their own falcons. At that time, British pilots were using homing pigeons to carry messages about the locations of crashed airplanes. The Royal Air Force was afraid that the peregrines would kill these valued pigeons. About 600 peregrines were killed in England between 1941 and 1945.

English soldiers release a pigeon during WW II.

homing pigeons (**hohm**·ing **pij**·uhnz)— pigeons that make their way home from great distances, often carrying messages

allies (**al**·iez)—friends

Threats From Humans

After the war, humans were the cause of other, more serious dangers to the falcon population. For example, some falconers would snatch very young birds out of their nests to train them. Often, these birds did not survive. Bird egg collectors were the source of another problem. These collectors considered peregrine eggs prize finds. The reason? The rarer the bird, the more valuable its eggs. (Roger Tory Peterson, a leading bird expert, said that no more than 5,000 peregrines have ever lived in the entire United States.) A Boston egg collector was known to have more than 700 peregrine eggs! And that's just one collector. There were many other large collections around the country.

These collectors defended their hobby. They argued that peregrines would lay other eggs to replace the ones taken. That sounds good, but often the next bunch of eggs would be taken by another collector. Bird experts warned that egg collectors could wipe out the peregrine population in America. The practice of collecting these eggs was finally outlawed.

A Scary Development

In 1962, an American bird expert named Joseph Hickey went to a meeting for scientists in New York. There, Hickey heard a scary rumor about peregrines in the northeastern United States. The rumor was that during 1962, not a single peregrine had hatched on the East Coast! Upon further study, he couldn't find even one peregrine nest in use in the eastern United States. What was happening?

The answer came a year later. That's when English expert Derek Ratcliffe reported that **aeries** in his

aeries (**air**·eez)—nests of birds of prey, built in high places

A peregrine falcon guards her eggs.

A peregrine feeds her chicks.

country also had been abandoned. From the 820 pairs Ratcliffe had measured in 1940, the number had dropped to 378. At that rate, it was estimated that within five years there would be no peregrines left!

Could the falconers and egg collectors have been responsible? Could there be another cause?

DDT: Another Cause

During the 1940s, scientists started to develop **pesticides**. DDT was one of those pesticides. After World War II, DDT was spread on crops to kill harmful insects. It was very successful in this and helped improve the production of food on crops where it was used. The problem was that DDT also harmed animals that it was not supposed to hurt. Scientists call such animals "non-target species." Ratcliffe suggested that DDT might be harming the falcons.

Hickey visited Ratcliffe in Europe in 1964. Together they searched the countryside for falcon nests. Ratcliffe explained to Hickey that he had seen peregrine parents eating their own eggs. Thin shells were the cause.

The falcons were hatching eggs with shells that were too thin. Because of this, the shells would break when the females sat on them. Once the young were dead, the parents would eat the eggs instead of wasting the "food." Hickey **speculated** that DDT was somehow causing the thin shells.

How were the peregrines getting the DDT? Smaller mammals were eating insects that were carrying DDT in their systems. When the falcons fed on these smaller animals, they were in turn harming themselves. They weren't dying, but they were being hurt in a very important way—DDT was harming their **reproductive system**. It was causing the falcons to hatch eggs with thin, breakable shells. That explained why the falcons were not having enough babies.

pesticides
(**pes**·ti·siedz)— chemicals used to kill pests, such as insects

speculated
(**spek**·yuh·lay·tid)— thought about; formed theories

reproductive system
(ree·pruh·**duk**·tiv sis·tuhm)—the parts of the body that produce offspring

Hickey returned to America and rapidly organized a conference to study the **fate** of peregrines. The results were grim. East of the Mississippi River, almost no peregrines were left. In the Rocky Mountains, only one third of the known nests were still occupied. Hickey knew that somehow he needed to prove Ratcliffe's theory that DDT was thinning falcon eggshells.

Proving the Theory

One way to prove the theory of the thinning eggshells was to compare present-day falcon eggs with eggs from the time before DDT was used. But where could Hickey find pre-DDT eggs?

Remember those egg collectors who were forced to stop collecting peregrine eggs? These same collectors were able to help Hickey by providing him with some of the eggs from their collections. But how could he collect new peregrine eggs? The practice was against the law in the United States. Hickey turned to outlaw collectors, who had continued to collect some of the eggs anyway. Hickey was now able to compare the weights of the eggs. He found that, indeed, the new egg shells were thinner. Further research proved that DDT was the cause.

Ospreys, like the peregrines, became sick from eating fish that often had DDT in them.

Other Birds in Danger

Peregrines were not the only birds nearly driven to extinction by DDT. The bald eagle, America's symbol, also was in danger. In the 1960s, robins were reported dropping dead on university campuses in the Midwest. The brown pelican and the osprey had eggshell thinning and population loss as well.

Pushing for a Ban

Based on these reports, scientists and environmentalists began pushing for a **ban** on DDT. But many farmers and public health officials opposed the idea. They argued that DDT killed a wide range of harmful insects. It reduced the number of insects carrying deadly diseases such as malaria, yellow fever, and typhus. And after all, its inventor, Dr. Paul Müller, was awarded the Nobel Prize for Medicine in 1948.

Nevertheless, the U.S. Environmental Protection Agency banned DDT in 1973. By then, more than two billion pounds of the chemical had been spread in the environment—nearly half a pound for every person on Earth at the time. The ban was good news, but was it too late for the peregrine falcons?

Peregrines Today

Project Peregrine, a research project, was started in 1970. It was run by Tom Cade, a Cornell University professor, and his graduate students. Together, they tried to breed captive peregrines. Their hope was to restore the species in the U.S. In 1974, Project Peregrine released the first captive-bred falcons into the wild! Two were put in nests in Colorado. Another pair was released on a campus of a state university in New York. By 1987, more than 2,000 young peregrines had been released in the United States, and more than 130 nesting pairs lived in 20 states from Maryland to California.

Today there are believed to be 1,400 nesting pairs of American peregrines and 4,000 pairs in Europe. The return of the peregrine from the brink of extinction is one of the greatest success stories in the modern age of endangered species.

A peregrine falcon family in their nest on a ledge of New York City's Metropolitan Life building

ban— a law forbidding something

Put Your Habits to Work in

Literature	Social Studies	Science	Math

Before I Read Habit:
Check it out!

Remember to look at how a section is organized **before** you read a chapter in your science textbook. One kind of organization is cause and effect.

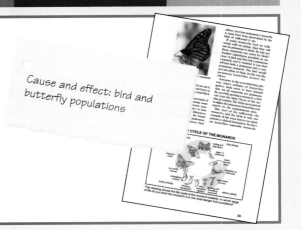

Cause and effect: bird and butterfly populations

While I Read Habit:
Stop and ask, "Does it make sense?"

Don't read a whole chapter! Stop and ask yourself if what you're reading makes sense. One way to find out is to try to figure out the causes of certain events.

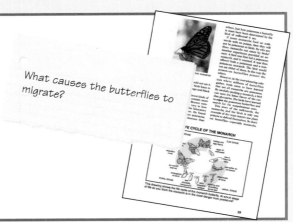

What causes the butterflies to migrate?

After I Read Habit:
React to what I've read.

You're not finished reading until you react to what you've read. You can do that by thinking about whether a different set of circumstances would have caused a different conclusion.

What if butterflies didn't migrate?

You may wish to use the **Put Your Habits to Work Sheet** (page 35 in your *Strategy Practice Book*) to practice these habits in your other reading.

Unit 6
Making Choices
Theme: Myself

In this unit, you will develop these 3 habits for all readers.

Before I Read Habit:
Think about what I know about the subject.

While I Read Habit:
Stop and ask, "How does it connect to what I know?"

After I Read Habit:
Use what I've read.

Learn 3 of the 9 Habits

In this unit, you will develop three habits—one for before you read, one for while you are reading, and one for after you finish reading. Start with **Before I Read**. Read the habit and strategy. Then read my notes below.

Before I Read

Which **HABIT** will I learn?
Think about what I know about the subject.
If I develop this habit, I will bring to mind what I already know about the subject. This gets me ready to connect what I read to what I know so I will understand it better.

Which **STRATEGY** will I use to learn this habit?
Preview the selection to see how these characters compare with characters in other stories I've read.

My Notes

- Strategy says to preview the story so I can compare the characters in this story with characters in other stories I've read.

- I looked at the title, pictures, and the first few sentences of the story and got the idea that this story has two friends who are plotting to cheat on some test.

- I know characters in other stories like this think they have outsmarted everyone with their great plan. Then they find out they're not as smart as they think!

A Foolproof Plan

by Steven Otfinoski

Don't get the idea I'm a regular class cheat. It's true that if the kid sitting next to me during a test happens to be a genius and has his test paper out in full view of half the class, I'm not going to look the other way. I mean, I'm not stupid. But that doesn't mean I spend half my waking moments thinking up new ways to cheat, either.

Before I continue, let me say that my best friend, Joe Luzzi, is a whiz at American history. It's not that he studies any more than I do (which isn't much), but he's got a head for dates and battles and stuff like that. They stick in his brain like glue. I guess it's just something you're born with, like a great pitching arm or a good sense of direction.

Now read the habit and strategy for **While I Read**. When you see 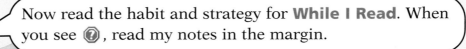, read my notes in the margin.

While I Read

Which **HABIT** will I learn?

Stop and ask, "How does it connect to what I know?"
If I develop this habit, I will think about how what I'm reading fits with what I know. This helps me understand the new material and remember it better.

Which **STRATEGY** will I use to learn this habit?
Try to picture myself in a character's place.

---

foolproof—so perfect that nothing can go wrong

Stop and Ask ?

How does it connect to what I know? Try to picture myself in a character's place.

Even though I don't cheat, I think I would be curious about Joe's foolproof plan and want to hear more about it. I've heard talk about ideas students have had that made me curious about whether they'd work.

Joe has Mr. Dooley for American history the period before I do. Mr. Dooley was planning a big multiple-choice test on the American Revolution on Monday for both classes. This got Joe and me to thinking after school that Friday about how neat it would be if he could somehow give me the answers to the test before I took it. It wasn't something we were actually planning to do. It was just kind of fun to think about it. But that was before Joe came up with his **foolproof** plan.

"You could slip me the answers between classes in the hall," I suggested.

"But my next class is in the other end of the building," Joe countered. "If I waited around for you, I'd be late for class, and that might get us both into trouble. It's too risky."

I pondered this.

"I could tape the answers under your chair before I left the room," Joe said. I shook my head. "No good. Someone is sure to see you. Mr. Dooley might even see you. Where would that put us?"

"You're right," sighed Joe. We both thought some more and suddenly Joe's eyes lit up like two Roman candles. I knew this time he had a real brainstorm.

"I've got it!" he said. "It's absolutely ingenious! Foolproof! I'm sorry I didn't think of it myself." ? *Strategy Alert!*

"Didn't you?" I asked, confused.

"No, I saw it in this spy movie on TV," Joe explained. "This spy had to pass on **vital** information to another spy, but they couldn't risk being seen together by the enemy. So the first spy left the information for the other spy in a public rest room."

"A rest room?"

"That's right."

I was beginning to think that Joe had lost his marbles. "What did he do?" I asked **sarcastically**. "Write the secret formula on the bathroom mirror?"

"No, of course not," Joe replied. "He put it in the paper-towel dispenser."

"You're kidding," I said.

"Listen, here's the plan," Joe began, lowering his voice as if he might be overheard by foreign agents. "I take the test on Monday morning and copy the answers down on a paper towel. The class ends. I go to the boys' room, open up the towel dispenser, and place the paper towel with the test answers in the dispenser."

"How are you going to do that?" I asked.

"I have a key," explained Joe. "Remember, I'm Mr. Jeeter's helper after school. He trusts me with it."

"Bad move on Mr. Jeeter's part." I smirked. Mr. Jeeter is the school custodian.

Joe ignored my wisecrack and went on. "I lock the towel in the dispenser and leave. You ask to be excused by Mr. Dooley to go to the boys' room before the test begins. You pull out a few paper towels from the dispenser and find the towel with the answers on it. You write them down on the palm of your hand and go back to class. Bingo! Instant A."

 Strategy Alert!

vital (**viet**·l)—very important

sarcastically (sahr·**kas**·tik·lee)—in a teasing way

Stop and Ask

How does it connect to what I know? Try to picture myself in a character's place.

I've seen other kids get caught cheating. I think if I were in this position, I would tell my friend that his idea is not worth the risk of getting caught.

skeptical
(**skep**·ti·kuhl)—unsure;
doubting

I looked **skeptical**. "It sounds good, but what happens if someone sees you putting the towel in the dispenser?"

"No one's going to see me," Joe insisted. "If someone's in there I'll just wait till they leave. Then I can lock the door. Mr. Jeeter does it all the time while he's cleaning the bathrooms. It'll only take me a minute or two to set the towel in place."

"What if Mr. Dooley doesn't let me out of class?" I asked.

"Have you ever seen Dooley turn anyone down for the bathroom?" Joe asked. I had to admit that our history teacher was a pushover when it came to such matters.

I still wasn't convinced. "What if somebody gets to the towel with the answers on it before I do?" I asked Joe.

"That won't happen," he replied. "I'll put the towel about a dozen in from the bottom. Nobody could go through them that fast before you got there. You just keep pulling them out until you reach the right one."

"What if someone else is in the boys' room?"

"Just wait until they leave," Joe said. "Relax, will you? I tell you, this is foolproof." *Strategy Alert!*

It sure sounded like it. I have to confess I was getting as excited as Joe about the whole thing. It wasn't so much the cheating part that captured my imagination as much as the thought of getting away with it so cleverly. Like a couple of professional spies, we went over the plan numerous times that weekend, even timing out the minutes between when Joe went to the boys' room and I left with the answers.

Stop and Ask ?

How does it connect to what I know? Try to picture myself in a character's place.

Joe is awfully sure of himself. I don't think I could be that sure of myself, especially to do something dishonest. Sometimes I get nervous when I know *exactly* what I'm doing!

On Monday morning, I walked into Mr. Dooley's history class with a confident **stride**. I hadn't even bothered to make my usual quick skim of the chapters we were to be tested on. I was planning to rely entirely on our foolproof plan. The risk made the whole adventure seem all the more exciting.

Mr. Dooley made a few announcements and briefly went over our next homework assignment. Then he told us to put away all books and papers. While he was speaking, I shot my hand up and asked if I could use the boys' room. Mr. Dooley looked a little uncertain, and for a moment I thought he was going to turn me down. But then the frown faded from his face and he told me to hurry back because the test was about to start. I promised I would as I took the green-colored hall pass from his hand.

The whole way to the boys' room my heart was beating against my rib cage like a **tom-tom**. The bathroom was empty, just as Joe predicted it would be. I went straight for the gleaming, metallic dispenser on the tiled wall and tugged on the first brown paper towel. It was blank. I pulled out two more. Not a jot of writing on either of them. Four, five, six . . .

Suddenly I heard the door to the boys' room swing open. I shoved the blank paper towels into the trash barrel and turned on the water. Around the corner of the metal **partition** appeared pimply-faced Roger Dubroski. Some break! Roger is a real nerd. The trouble is, he doesn't know it. He thinks he's just a regular guy like Joe or me and he tries to act the part. A conversation with Roger gives new meaning to the word *boring*. He was the last person on earth I needed to see right then. *Strategy Alert!*

"Hey, Fred. How's it going?" Roger asked. I kept my end of the conversation to a minimum and Roger chatted away as he carefully examined the newest zit on his face. I hardly heard a word he said. All my attention was focused on the paper-towel dispenser.

stride (stried)—a walk with long steps

tom-tom—a small drum, beat with a steady rhythm

partition (pahr·**tish**·uhn)—a divider

Stop and Ask ?

How does it connect to what I know? Try to picture myself in a character's place.

If I were in this situation, I would panic if someone came into the bathroom. I also know how it feels to be stuck talking to someone who goes on and on like Roger. I would want him to leave.

As Roger talked, I washed my hands in slow motion. Then I pulled out another towel—it was blank—and wiped them off. I was determined to keep wiping them until Roger was on his way out the door. Do you know how hard it is to wipe your hands for that long? Try it sometime. But Roger, bless him, didn't stop talking long enough to take any notice of how silly I looked.

He washed his own hands and then pulled out a towel. I looked at the wet towel in his hands in horror. It was covered in blue ink! Roger Dubroski was wiping his dirty, cruddy hands all over *my* answers to Mr. Dooley's history test! I watched helplessly as he rolled the towel into a small, wet ball and pitched it toward the trash barrel. He missed, of course.

"Nuts!" exclaimed Roger. "Gotta practice that foul shot. How about shooting some hoops after school, Fred?"

"I don't think so," I said lamely, grateful to see that Roger wasn't bothering to pick up the towel. I was afraid he'd notice the writing on it.

"Well, I'd like to stay and chat till lunch," said Roger breezily, "but I gotta get back to biology. We're **dissecting** frogs today."

"Sounds like fun," I said, faking interest.

"You said it," laughed Roger. "Betty Foreman nearly upchucked when Ms. Chang demonstrated the first **incision**!"

I would've given anything that moment to be upchucking in Ms. Chang's biology class over a dead frog or any other small animal you can mention instead of returning to Mr. Dooley's history test.

dissecting (di·**sek**·ting)— cutting apart to study closely

incision (in·**sizh**·uhn)— a cut, especially in relation to surgery

Roger finally left and I snatched up the paper towel from the floor. It was a mess. The blue ink was running all over the place. I spread the paper towel carefully on top of the flat soap dispenser and prayed that no one else would come in to disturb me. (They didn't.) Under careful examination, I was relieved to find that only a few of the answers were totally **undecipherable**. All the rest were blotchy but still readable.

I neatly wrote each lettered answer on the palm of my left hand with my trusty ballpoint. They just fit. Then I flushed the **incriminating** evidence down the toilet, like any good spy would, and hustled back to class.

Mr. Dooley gave me a slightly **askew** look over the top of his tortoise-shell glasses as I walked in. I handed him back the hall pass and he handed me a test. *Strategy Alert!*

"You'd better get busy, Mr. Lendleman," Mr. Dooley said. "Your classmates have a head start on you."

I nodded and went back to my desk, smiling secretly. I skillfully managed to sneak a peek at each answer on my palm and wrote it down in the appropriate space. I took my time, staring off into space occasionally and gnawing thoughtfully on the eraser at the end of my pencil. I wanted to put on a good show for Mr. Dooley, who was watching us with eagle eyes from his desk. When I got to the three questions I hadn't the answers for, I read the questions and found, to my great surprise, that I actually knew the answers to two of them.

When the time was up, Mr. Dooley asked us to put down our pencils and pass our tests in. I followed the instructions and then gave my left palm a few rubs. The sweat from my other hand reduced the answers on my palm to a blue smudge.

undecipherable (un·di·**sie**·fuhr·uh·buhl)— not able to make meaning of

incriminating (in·**krim**·uh·nay·ting)— showing that someone is guilty

askew (uh·**skyoo**)—off to one side; not straight

Stop and Ask ?

How does it connect to what I know? Try to picture myself in a character's place.

If I were in Fred's place and thought the teacher gave me a funny look, I would be too nervous to cheat. I would forget the whole plan.

warily (**wair**·uh·lee)—
in a careful way

Stop and Ask **?**

How does it connect
to what I know? Try
to picture myself in a
character's place.

· · · · · · · · · ·

 If I were Fred, I
would have felt
worried—not just
about doing poorly
on the test but
about getting in
trouble for cheating.
I know people who
have gotten in big
trouble for cheating.
It's just not worth it.

vicinity (vi·**sin**·i·tee)—
nearby area

As the bell rang, I got up from my chair, full of confidence.

"How did you do?" asked Susan Anders, who sat across from me.

"Oh, all right, I think," I said, grinning ear to ear.

"I don't think I did too well," she sighed. "I hardly studied at all. I have a friend in the previous class and she gave me a few answers in advance. I thought it might help, but it didn't of course."

I was truly surprised. It appeared that Joe and I weren't the only two-some who had plotted to make good use of Mr. Dooley's back-to-back testing. I had to play it cool, though. I didn't want to let on about our plan, not even to Susan.

"Why didn't it help?" I asked her **warily**.

"How could it, when Mr. D. pulled that fast one on us?" replied the girl.

I stopped dead in my tracks, right in the middle of the crowded hallway.

"A fast one?" I repeated.

Susan looked at me, puzzled for a moment. Then she smiled. "Oh, that's right, I forgot," she said. "You were out of the room when Mr. Dooley announced that he had switched the questions around on our test to discourage any cheating between classes." **?** *Strategy Alert!*

I could feel my heart sinking to the general **vicinity** of my toes. "Are you serious?" I said.

"Yeah," replied Susan. "So much for my free answers. Oh well, I'm glad you did well, Fred. Next time I guess I'll try studying."

That makes two of us, I thought.

> Congratulations! You finished reading. Now read the habit and strategy for **After I Read**. Then read my notes below.

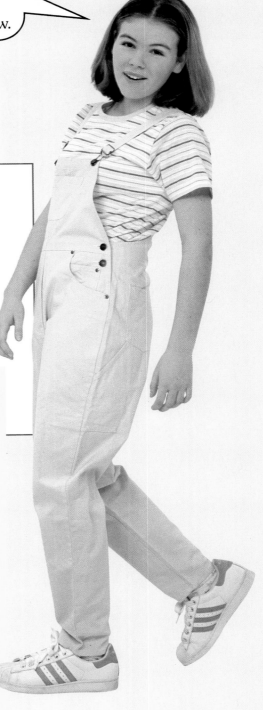

After I Read

Which **HABIT** will I learn?
Use what I've read.
If I develop this habit, I will think about how I can apply what I just read to my schoolwork and my life. This makes reading really useful.

Which **STRATEGY** will I use to learn this habit?
Decide how I can apply what I read to a different situation.

My Notes

- Strategy says that I should decide how I can apply what I read to a different situation.

- Well, I know it's always better to be honest and not take what looks like the easy way out. If Fred had been honest, he would have done better on the test. He even said he knew some of the answers!

- If anyone asks me to do something dishonest, I know I won't. It's not worth the risk. I know I would not like myself if I were dishonest.

Now, it's time to practice the three habits and strategies you learned when you read "A Foolproof Plan." Start with **Before I Read**. Look at the box below. It should look familiar! Reread the habit you will practice. Reread the strategy you will use—then do it!

Before I Read

Which **HABIT** will I practice?
Think about what I know about the subject.
If I develop this habit, I will bring to mind what I already know about the subject. This gets me ready to connect what I read to what I know so I will understand it better.

Which **STRATEGY** will I use to practice this habit?
Preview the selection to see how these characters compare with characters in other stories I've read.

 Use the **Before I Read Strategy Sheet** for "Amanda and the Wounded Birds" (page 36 in your *Strategy Practice Book*) to think about what you know about the subject.

Amanda
and the Wounded Birds

by Colby Rodowsky

psychotherapist
(sie·koh·**ther**·uh·pist)—
a person who treats
others who have mental,
emotional, and nervous
disorders

*Her mother's radio program provides sensitive, helpful advice for emotionally troubled callers. But having a famous **psychotherapist** for a mother is no comfort to Amanda. . . .*

It's not that my mother doesn't understand, because she does. In fact, she understands so well, and so much, and so single-mindedly, that half the time she goes around with a glazed look in her eyes and forgets to get her hair cut, and go to the dentist and that we're almost out of toilet paper or tuna fish.

She makes her living understanding, which may make more sense when I tell you that my mother is Dr. Emma Hart. Now, if that doesn't help, then probably, like me until my consciousness was raised, you've always thought of radio as the place to hear the Top 40 or sometimes the weather report when you're heading for the shore on a summer Friday afternoon. But just try twiddling the dial and you'll find her, way over to the left on the band, next to the country and western station.

Read the habit and strategy below. Look for the *Strategy Alerts!* as you continue to read.

While I Read

Which **HABIT** will I practice?
Stop and ask, "How does it connect to what I know?"
If I develop this habit, I will think about how what I'm reading fits with what I know. This helps me understand the new material and remember it better.

Which **STRATEGY** will I use to practice this habit?
Try to picture myself in a character's place.

 Use the **While I Read Strategy Sheet** for "Amanda and the Wounded Birds" (page 37 in your *Strategy Practice Book*) as you read.

establish (i·**stab**·lish)—
to set up

stoically
(**stoh**·i·kuh·lee)—
in a calm, patient way

Maybe what I should do is go back a little and explain. You see, my mother is a psychotherapist, which means that she counsels people and tries to help them find ways of dealing with their problems. She's also a widow. My father died when I was a baby, and sometimes I try to imagine what it must have been like for her, taking care of a baby alone and trying to **establish** a practice all at the same time. One thing I'm sure of is that knowing Mom, she handled it gracefully, and **stoically,** and with that funny way she has of biting her lower lip so that for all her hanging-in-there attitude she still looks like a ten-year-old kid—the kind you want to do something for because she's not always whining or sniffling. I guess you'd have to say that as much as possible my mother is in charge of her own life, which is the way she tries to get the people who call in to her on the radio to be.

The way the radio program got started was that several years ago the producer was looking for something to put on in the late afternoon when people were mostly fixing dinner or driving carpool or just sitting with their feet up. It wasn't exactly prime time. Then he remembered how he'd heard Mom speak at a dinner once and had thought at the time that putting someone like her on radio would be a real public service. Besides, the ratings couldn't be any lower than they had been for the Handy Home Fixit show he'd had on before. Anyway, he tracked her down, arranged for a test, and then Mom was on the air.

I never will forget that first show. I mean, there was my mother's voice coming out of our kitchen radio, sounding slightly **frantic** and giving those first callers more than they bargained for: I guess she was afraid if she let them off the line there wouldn't *be* any more. That day even the producer called with a question. And the boy in the studio who went for coffee. But Mom hung in there, and calls continued to come in, and then they started backing up, and it wasn't long before people opened by saying, "I didn't think I'd *ever* get through to you." After only a month on the air the Emma Hart show went from one hour to two; and the way I figured it, a lot of people were eating dinner later than they ever had before. Including us.

Mom really cared about the people who telephoned her, and almost right from the beginning she was calling them her "wounded birds." Not on the air, of course, and *never* to anyone but me. I got used to her looking up in the middle of dinner or from watching the late news on TV and saying, "I hope my wounded bird with the abusive husband will get herself into counseling" or "The wounded bird with those children who walk all over her had better learn to **assert** herself before it's too late." And *I* sure learned not to joke around: once I referred to one of her callers as a **fractured** canary and almost started World War III. ⓘ *Strategy Alert!*

frantic (**fran**·tik)— overexcited

assert (uh·**surt**)—to express oneself in a forceful way

fractured (**frak**·chuhrd)—broken

> **Stop and Ask** ❓
>
> How does it connect to what I know? Try to picture myself in a character's place.

Not long after this, things really started to happen. First, Mom's show was moved to a better time slot. Then it was syndicated, so that she wasn't just on the air here but in a bunch of other cities, too. The way "Doonesbury" and "Dick Tracy" are in a bunch of newspapers. Now, I have to say that for the most part my mother's pretty cool about things, but the day she found out that the Emma Hart show was being syndicated she just about flipped. She called me from the studio and told me to meet her at the Terrace Garden for dinner, to be sure and get spiffed up because we were going all out.

During dinner Mom spent a lot of time staring into the candlelight and smiling to herself. Finally, she said, "Just think of all those people who'll be listening now." And let me tell you, I *was* thinking about them, and it worried me a lot. I mean the way I saw it, there were going to be even more problems: more victims who were **downtrodden** or misunderstood.

More stories about people who had been abused or who had kids on drugs or dropping out, or **ne'er-do-well** relatives moving in. But when I tried to say that, Mom was suddenly all attention. "Don't be silly, Amanda. It's the same amount of time and the same number of calls—you'll hardly notice any difference. Only now I'll have wounded birds in Phoenix [**fee**·nix] and Pittsburgh and Philadelphia."

In one way she was right: the show sounded pretty much the same. (Except that *I* found out that when your husband/friend walks out on you it hurts as much in Peoria as it does in Perth Amboy.)

In another way she was wrong: she was busier than she had ever been before, what with traveling and lecturing and doing guest shows from other cities. For a while there, it was as if I was spending as much time at my best friend Terri's as I was at my own house. Then eventually Mom decided I could stay at our place when she had to be out of town, as long as Terri stayed there with me, which wasn't as good or as bad as it sounds, because Terri lives right across the street and her mother has X-ray eyes. I mean we can hardly manage to reach for our favorite breakfast of ice cream with an orange juice chaser before her mother is on the telephone telling us to eat cornflakes instead—and to wash the dishes.

downtrodden
(**down**·trod·n)—
disadvantaged; without privilege

ne'er-do-well
(**nair**·doo·wel)—lazy; irresponsible

Sometimes I felt that life was nothing but a revolving door: Mom going out while I was coming in. I know there are some kids who would've thought I was lucky, but the thing about my mother is that she's okay. And I wanted to see more of her. Besides that, I needed to talk to her. I don't know why, but all of a sudden it seemed that things were piling up around me. No major crises, you understand. Nothing that would exactly stop traffic. **?** *Strategy Alert!*

I'll give you an example.

Take my friend Terri. I have a terrible feeling that she has a secret crush on my boyfriend Josh. If she does, it would be a disaster, because how could we really be friends anymore? But then again, how could Terri and I *not* be friends? I'm not sure *why* I think this, unless it's because she gets quiet and acts bored when I talk about him a lot—the way you do when you don't want to let on about liking someone. I mean she couldn't *really* be bored. Could she?

Then there's Miss Spellman, my English teacher, who has this really atrocious [uh·**troh**·shuhs] breath and is forever leaning into people as she reads poetry in class. Imagine somebody breathing garbage fumes on you as she recites Emily Dickinson. If something doesn't happen soon, I may never like poetry again.

Stop and Ask **?**

How does it connect to what I know? Try to picture myself in a character's place.

a.s.a.p.—stands for "as soon as possible"

syndrome (**sin**·drohm)— a collection of symptoms that appear together

Now, maybe these aren't world problems, any more than the incident with the guidance counselor was, but it bugged me all the same. Our school has an obsession about students getting into *good* colleges **a.s.a.p.** and knowing what they want to do with the rest of their lives (Terri and I call it the life-packaging **syndrome**). Anyway, this particular day I was coming out of gym on my way to study hall when Mr. Burnside, the guidance counselor, stopped me and started asking me all this stuff, like what my career goals were and had I decided what I wanted to major in in college.

What I said (only politer than it sounds here) was that how did I know what I wanted to major in when I didn't even know where I wanted to go to college. Mr. Burnside got a wild look in his eyes and started opening and closing his mouth so that all I could see was a shiny strand of spit running between his top and bottom teeth while he lectured me on how I was going about this whole college thing the wrong way. He said I should come into the guidance office someday and let him feed me into the computer—well, not me exactly, but stuff like my grades, extracurricular activities, and whether or not I needed financial aid.

"And what does your mother say?" he asked as he rooted in his pocket for a late pass to get me into study hall. "You'll certainly have it easier than anybody else in your class, or the school either for that matter—living with Dr. Emma Hart." He laughed that horselaugh of his and slapped me on the back. "She'll get right to the *Hart* of it." Another laugh. "Anybody else'd have to call her on the telephone." His laughter seemed to follow me all the way to study hall. I even heard it bouncing around in my head as I settled down to do my Spanish.

"Anybody else'd have to call her on the telephone," he had said.

Why not? I thought as I was walking home from school.

Why not? I asked myself when Josh and I were eating popcorn and playing a board game on the living room floor that night.

And pretty soon *why not?* changed to *when?* The answer to that one was easy though, because spring vacation was only a week and a half away and that would give me the perfect opportunity.

The funny thing was that once I'd decided to do it, I never worried about getting through. Maybe that was because I'd heard Mom say plenty of times that they always liked it when kids called into the show, and I guess I figured that unless everybody on spring vacation decided to call the Dr. Emma Hart Show, I wouldn't have any trouble. Besides, I practiced in the shower making my voice huskier than usual and just a little breathless, hoping that it would sound sincere and make an impression on Jordan, the guy who screens the calls and tries for just the right balance of men, women, and kids, with not too much emphasis on busted romances as opposed to anxiety attacks. **?** *Strategy Alert!*

The next funny thing was that once I'd made up my mind to call Dr. Emma Hart, I began to feel like a wounded bird myself, and I was suddenly awfully glad that she cared about them the way she did. I had a little trouble deciding what I wanted to ask her on the show, and even before I could make up my mind I began to think of other things that bothered me too. Not problems, but stuff I'd like to talk over with Mom. Like Vietnam, for example. I'd watched *Apocalypse Now* on TV and there was a lot I didn't understand. And what about the sixties?—was Mom ever involved in **sit-ins** or walkouts or any of that? I somehow doubted it, but it would be important to know for sure. Finally it came to me: what I wanted to ask Dr. Hart about was not being able to talk to Mom because there she was all wrapped up with her wounded birds. Only the whole thing got confusing, one being the other and all.

Stop and Ask **?**

How does it connect to what I know? Try to picture myself in a character's place.

sit-ins—gatherings in which people sit in inconvenient places to get attention for causes

intense (in·**tens**)—
showing great effort

Stop and Ask

How does it connect
to what I know? Try
to picture myself in a
character's place.

Anyway, I did it. I put the call in just before eleven on the Monday morning of spring vacation and almost chickened out when Jordan answered. I had met him a couple of times down at the studio, and I could almost see him now, looking like some kind of an **intense** juggler who is trying to keep everything going at once. I heard my voice, as if it were coming from somewhere far away, giving my name as Claire (it's my middle name) and outlining my problem. When I got finished, Jordan said that he was putting me on hold and not to go away, that Dr. Hart would be with me shortly.

And all of a sudden she was. I mean, there I was talking to my own mother and telling her how I couldn't talk to my mother, and how the things I wanted to talk to her about weren't actually big deals anyway, but still—. ❓ *Strategy Alert!*

Dr. Hart let me go on for a while and then she broke in and said that it was important for me to know that my concerns were as real as anybody else's and it sounded as if my mother and I had a pretty good relationship that had just gotten a little off the track and what I had to do was be really up-front with her and let her know how I felt. Then she suggested that I make a date with my mother for lunch so that I could tell her (Mom) exactly what I'd told her (Dr. Emma Hart), and that I should be sure to call back and let her know how it worked out.

After that I said, "Okay," and "Thank you." Then I hung up.

The only trouble was that as soon as Mom got home that day I knew it wasn't going to work.

She was sort of coming unglued. It had been a bad day, she told me. One of her private patients was in the **midst** of a crisis; the producer of the show was having a fight with his wife and wanted to tell Mom all about it. She had a dinner speech to give Saturday night and didn't have a thought about what to say, and my uncle Alex had called from Scranton to ask Mom to try to talk some sense into his teenage son, who was driving them all crazy.

Then she looked at me and said, "Thank heavens you've got it all together."

Talk about guilt. Right away I knew I was going to break rule number one: I wasn't going to be able to be up-front. 🛑 *Strategy Alert!*

The thing was, I knew I couldn't take what was already one rotten week for Mom and dump all my problems (which seemed to be getting bigger by the minute) on her. Even though I felt like I was going to explode.

By Friday I knew I needed another talk with Dr. Hart. After all, she'd said to call back, hadn't she?

Getting through Jordan was even easier the second time. All I had to say was that I'd spoken to Dr. Hart earlier in the week and that she'd said to let her know what happened.

"Oh, good, a success story," Jordan said right away, jumping to conclusions. I guess he knew what kind of a week it had been too. "Hold on; Dr. Hart will be with you soon," he said.

And there was Dr. Emma Hart again. And suddenly there *I* was, unloading about how what she suggested wasn't going to work.

"Why not?" she wanted to know. "Did you try?"

"Yes—no," I said. Then I was going on again, all about Bad-Breath Spellman, the guidance counselor, and how maybe my best friend had a thing for my boyfriend. She kept steering me back to the subject of my mother and why I hadn't arranged to have lunch with her.

I said that my mother had had a bad week. That she was swamped, **preoccupied,** distracted, and running behind. And then it happened. I mean, I heard the words sliding off my lips and couldn't stop them. I said, "The thing about my mother is that she has all these wounded birds who have really important problems and they take up all the time she has."

midst—the middle part of

Stop and Ask ❓

How does it connect to what I know? Try to picture myself in a character's place.

preoccupied (pree·**ok**·yuh·pied)—deep in thought

Stop and Ask ?

How does it connect to what I know? Try to picture myself in a character's place.

A silence ballooned up between us and was so loud I couldn't hear anything else—and if you know anything about radio, you know that the worst thing that can happen is silence. It lasted forever, and while it was going on I gave serious thought to running away from home, or at least hanging up. ? *Strategy Alert!*

When Mom finally spoke, her voice sounded choked, as if she had swallowed a gumball.

"We've been talking to Claire this morning, who is really Amanda," she said. "And one of the things we talk a lot about on this show is saying what you have to say—even if that's not always easy. Are you still there, Amanda?"

"Yes," I squeaked.

"If I know Amanda," my mother went on, "she would rather have run away, or hung up, but instead she did something harder. She hung on."

I gulped.

"Amanda is my daughter, and it seems we have some things to talk about, so what I'm going to do is ask my assistant to make a reservation for lunch at the Terrace Garden." Then it sounded as though Mom had moved in closer to the microphone and was speaking just to me. "If you hurry, Amanda, I'll meet you at 1:30. So we can talk."

And we did: about Bad-Breath Spellman, and Terri, and how it's okay not to know what I want to do with the rest of my life.

We talked about saving the whales, and our two weeks at the shore this summer, and how someday we're going to Ireland. About books and movies and the time in fourth grade when I got the chicken pox and Mom caught them from me.

And we talked about how we had missed talking to each other and what we could do about it.

We ate lunch slowly, and took ages deciding on dessert, and ages more eating it.

We sat there all afternoon, until the light streaking in the windows changed from yellow to a deep, burning gold and the busboys started setting the tables for dinner.

Now that you've finished reading, review the **After I Read** habit below. Think about what you read in "Amanda and the Wounded Birds" as you practice the strategy.

After I Read

Which **HABIT** will I practice?
Use what I've read.
If I develop this habit, I will think about how I can apply what I just read to my schoolwork and my life. This makes reading really useful.

Which **STRATEGY** will I use to practice this habit?
Decide how I can apply what I read to a different situation.

Use the **After I Read Strategy Sheet** for "Amanda and the Wounded Birds" (page 38 in your *Strategy Practice Book*) to help you use what you've read.

Apply 3 of the 9 Habits

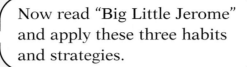

Now read "Big Little Jerome" and apply these three habits and strategies.

Before I Read

Which **HABIT** will I apply?
Think about what I know about the subject.

Which **STRATEGY** will I use to apply this habit?
Preview the selection to see how these characters compare with characters in other stories I've read.

While I Read

Which **HABIT** will I apply?
Stop and ask, "How does it connect to what I know?"

Which **STRATEGY** will I use to apply this habit?
Try to picture myself in a character's place.

After I Read

Which **HABIT** will I apply?
Use what I've read.

Which **STRATEGY** will I use to apply this habit?
Decide how I can apply what I read to a different situation.

Use the **Self-Assessment Sheet** for "Big Little Jerome" (pages 39–40 in your *Strategy Practice Book*) to see how well you can apply the habits and strategies.

Big
Little
Jerome

by Budge Wilson

Jerome Seaboyer was always small. He was born in the village of Periwinkle Pond on the South Shore of Nova Scotia [**noh**·vuh **skoh**·shuh], where his father was a fisherman, and where everybody knew something about everybody else. On his arrival, the other mothers gathered around and clucked, "Oh my, oh my! So little. I hope he's okay." They held their own big, sturdy babies **smugly,** and looked with pity at his mother.

Mrs. Seaboyer, just home from the hospital with her tiny bundle, felt anger rise in her throat and said coolly, "He's fine. He's perfect. He's beautiful." Secretly she thought the other babies fat and lumpy, but she did not say so. Nor did she admire their eyes or their feet or their gassy smiles. Instead she said, "I'm beginning to feel a bit tired," and held open the front door. The women left, well satisfied with their visit. But small lines appeared between Mrs. Seaboyer's eyebrows. She sat down on the bottom step of the stairway, and worried. She worried off and on for the rest of her life.

smugly (**smug**·lee)—in a conceited, self-important way

Even when Jerome started to get older, he kept on being small. He walked by himself at nine months, and Mrs. Rhodenizer [**roh**·duh·nie·zuhr] said it gave her the creeps to see anything that little walking around. Mrs. Seaboyer took note of the fact that Harrison Rhodenizer was fourteen months old and still couldn't do anything but sit. She didn't say so, right out. She smiled sweetly at Mrs. Rhodenizer and asked, "Should I push the sharp things to the back of the table so that Harrison can't hurt himself?" knowing full well that she could have put hand grenades on the table without Harrison's being in any danger at all.

When Jerome was finally old enough to go to school, Mrs. Seaboyer waved good-bye as he boarded the school bus for the first time. She wondered how he could possibly survive at school. He looked young enough to be in diapers, and there he was, leaving her sheltering arms for seven hours every day.

Actually, Mrs. Seaboyer could have relaxed. Jerome did just fine. At five and a half years old, he was full of fun and always knew how to make people laugh, even on foggy days and during hurricanes. He was very smart, and he sailed through school with high marks and bright ideas. He was a good swimmer and a quick runner, and he won all the track-and-field ribbons for any event requiring speed. The gym instructor named him "Grease" because, he said, he was like greased lightning. But even when Jerome was in fourth grade, people would stop him on the road, stoop down on a level with his nose, and ask, "Do you go to school yet, little boy?" He used to laugh and say, "Sure! I'm in fourth grade!" and then wait to enjoy their looks of surprise. Jerome was a very happy person.

But this state of affairs could not go on forever. Unlike Jerome, Mrs. Seaboyer could look ahead, and maybe that's why those lines never left the center of her forehead. She knew that one day Jerome would wake up and realize that when a man gets older, a lot of things are easier and more pleasant if he's tall. Sure enough, the day after his thirteenth birthday, Jerome met Mrs. Rhodenizer in Dorey's **Variety Store**. She looked down at him and said, "My heavenly days, Jerome! Still so *small*! For goodness sakes, you'll be in high school next year and all the girls will be taller than you. Aren't you *ever* going to get any bigger?" Jerome felt a cold wind blow across his heart. He didn't know what to say. He looked for a second into her **nearsighted** eyes; they were peering down at him through glasses so thick they looked like the bottom of **pop** bottles. He felt like an insect stuck on a pin. Then he lowered his gaze roughly in the direction of her belly button. "Maybe so. Maybe no," he chanted lightly. Mrs. Rhodenizer thought his reply was rude, and said so. Of course, Harrison Rhodenizer was more than five feet six already and his voice was starting to change. He also did poorly in school, fell all over his feet, and was as fat as a pudding.

From that moment on, Jerome became a secret worrier. He realized that what Mrs. Rhodenizer had said was absolutely correct. The girls were taller than he was, including Andrea Doucette [doo·**set**], the prettiest girl in his class. Andrea sat in front of him at school, and he loved to look at the back of her head and the way the sun shone on her long, straight, blond hair. Sometimes he would just sit there and think up words to describe it: honey, gold, wheat, sunshine, dandelion.

It is true that Andrea seemed to like Jerome. When she was class president, she always chose him first for spelling bees and relay races. But this was middle school. What about next year? Being short could really begin to matter in high school.

variety store
(vuh·**rie**·i·tee stor)—a retail store carrying many different kinds of items

nearsighted
(**near**·siet·id)—trouble seeing things that are far away clearly

pop—soda

Jerome started locking himself in the bathroom in order to measure his height against the towel rack, and to inspect his face for signs of whiskers. The towel rack stayed in the same place, and so did Jerome. His small handsome face was as smooth as paper. His body was well built and muscular—all four foot six of it. He had thrilling dreams in which he was seven feet tall, his face lost behind a thick, jet-black beard. In these dreams he spent a lot of time saving less gifted swimmers from drowning—people like Harrison Rhodenizer, who couldn't swim a stroke. And night after night he carried Andrea Doucette out of burning buildings, single-handed.

Jerome started to develop lines between *his* eyebrows. Outwardly he was the same as ever: full of jokes, everyone's pal, the life of the party, athletic, smart. But inside, he had sinking feelings. He could visualize a long life ahead of him as an undersized **bachelor,** reading his books and eating his dinners alone in a pint-sized house, while other men came home to tall, loving wives and **enormous** families.

Mrs. Seaboyer, who could usually tell exactly what Jerome was thinking, did all she was able to. She searched for clothes in small sizes that did not seem like kindergarten styles. She fed him masses of vitamins and prayed for growth. She read articles on the mysteries of the **pituitary gland**. She told him that he looked, and was, marvelous. Jerome admired her strategy, but he saw through it.

His father, for his part, pretended his son was of normal size, and taught him all the fishing lore he knew. Jerome learned about the **inshore fisheries,** could dress a fish with flair, knew how to recognize the right wood for making lobster traps, and could mend a net and prop up a wharf as well as anybody. He was as prepared for life as it was possible for him to be. But he heard the women whisper when he passed, "A sweet boy! Sad!" And he hated it when the men referred to him as "a nice little feller."

Then his voice changed. It happened gradually, with the usual embarrassing cracks and lurches in his vocal chords. But soon—much sooner than with the other boys—his voice was complete. And it was magnificent.

bachelor
(**bach**·uh·luhr)—an unmarried man

enormous
(i·**nor**·muhs)—very great in number

pituitary gland
(pi·**too**·i·ter·ee gland)— the organ in the body that controls growth

inshore fisheries
(**in**·shor **fish**•uh•rees)— places near shore where fish can be caught

It was deep and rich and powerful. He sang in the bathtub at top volume. He thought up excuses to talk in class. His shouted instructions on the basketball court and at the skating rink were thundering.

But once the first thrill was over, Jerome's vocal talent threw him further into fits of depression. The contrast between what he was and what he was not was so obvious that he felt more ridiculous than he had before. What was this king-sized voice doing coming from a little boy's body? To add to his problems, things kept coming up at school that worried him. Things like the Christmas dance. Jerome knew he would sit at home and watch TV and wish he were dead. He decided to **concoct** an illness. Twenty-four-hour stomach flu would do. Certainly no girl would want to dance around the gym with *him*.

One Thursday afternoon, Jerome met Andrea Doucette as he was leaving the variety store. They were talking about homework and the usual things, when suddenly Andrea blurted out, "Jerome, would you like to go to the dance with me?" He was stunned. All he could think to say was, "Oh. Well. Okay. I guess so." Then he turned and left her standing on the steps of the store. In a kind of trance, he walked as far as the **breakwater**. He stopped then, and stared out at the horizon, full of amazement. Finally he swung around and looked at Andrea. She was staggering under the weight of two bags of groceries, and suddenly they went crashing to the ground. When Jerome rushed back to help, he saw tears in her eyes. Picking up the groceries, he asked, "What's the matter? Why are you crying?"

concoct (kuhn·**kokt**)— to invent; to make up

breakwater (**brayk**·waw·tuhr)— a wall that protects a shoreline from waves

"I'm not, *really*," she said, blinking her eyes. "It's just that I'm shy and you're popular and athletic, and I'm just me. And all you said was, 'Oh. Well. Okay. I guess so.' It was like you slapped me."

Jerome just looked at her. He looked *up* at her, of course, because she was taller than he was. Then he told her he had been too surprised to say anything. As he carried her groceries home for her, he talked about being short, and how awful it was.

Andrea stopped in her tracks and stared at him. "What do you want, Jerome Seaboyer?" she asked, brown eyes flashing. *"Everything?"* Then she looked even fiercer, and went on, "Who do you want to be, if you don't want to be you? Harrison Rhodenizer? Robert MacIntosh? Your father? Ewart Boutilier [bou•ti•lee•**ay**]? Oh, for Pete's sake!"

Suddenly Jerome needed to be alone. He thrust the groceries down on Andrea's porch and muttered, "Gotta go. See you tomorrow." Then he rushed home and picked up his ice skates, and ran all the way to Little Gull Lake.

The lake was smooth and untouched. Most people liked to skate on Morrison's Pond, because it was bigger. But here, there was not a mark on the ice. He put on his skates and went out to the rock that broke the surface in the middle of the lake. There he sat down to think. He was in possession of a certain thought, and he needed enough quiet to look at all sides of it. *Did* he, as Andrea had suggested, want *everything*? Well, yes, as a matter of fact, he did. He knew he had almost all of the things that most people wanted out of life, but he longed for that one special, important, extra thing that would make everything perfect.

Jerome rested his chin on his fist and thought some more. Okay then, did he want to be Harrison Rhodenizer? Poor old, dumb old Harrison Rhodenizer, who had to put up with his nosy mother? No, *thanks*.

And Robert MacIntosh? No. He was tall, but he had rotten teeth and his parents drank all the time. His own father, then? A great guy, of course, but *old*. Half of his life was over. He did nothing but work. What about Ewart Boutilier? That was trickier. Andrea must have thrown in that name to make him think. *Really* think. Ewart Boutilier was the tallest boy in the class, handsome, popular, and intelligent. The girls chased after him, or stood around in the halls and giggled when he walked by. He was even *nice*. Jerome thought hard about Ewart. And then, suddenly, he knew. He would like to have *parts* of Ewart—his height, and his fatal charm with the girls. But he did not want to *be* Ewart Boutilier. He, Jerome Seaboyer, wanted to be Jerome Seaboyer. He wanted his own parents, his own special friends, his brains, his sense of humor, his house, his own thoughts and feelings and loves—even his own fears and hates and worries. He wanted to be himself.

Jerome felt as though a ton had been lifted from the back of his neck. He rose from the rock and started to skate, wildly, beautifully, around the lake. He skated in curves and circles, jumping over rocks and spinning around cracks, and then racing at dangerous speeds from one side of the lake to the other. He threw his arms wide, and with his beautiful voice shouted to the trees, "I'm *me*! I'm *me*!" Up above, the sky was blue and cloudless and high. Jerome Seaboyer felt as though he could touch it.

Put Your Habits to Work in

| Literature | Social Studies | Science | Math |

Before I Read Habit:
Think about what I know about the subject.

Look over a piece of literature before you read it. Try to get some idea about how the characters in this story compare with characters in other stories you have read.

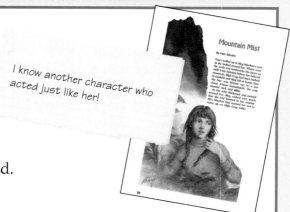

I know another character who acted just like her!

While I Read Habit:
Stop and ask, "How does it connect to what I know?"

Remember to stop every once in a while and ask yourself how what you're reading connects to what you know. One way to find out is to picture yourself in a character's place. What would you do in that situation?

I would feel that way, too.

After I Read Habit:
Use what I've read.

You're not finished reading until you use what you've read. You can do that by deciding how you can apply what you read to a different situation.

Reading this has helped me understand...

 You may wish to use the **Put Your Habits to Work Sheet** (page 41 in your *Strategy Practice Book*) to practice these habits in your other reading.

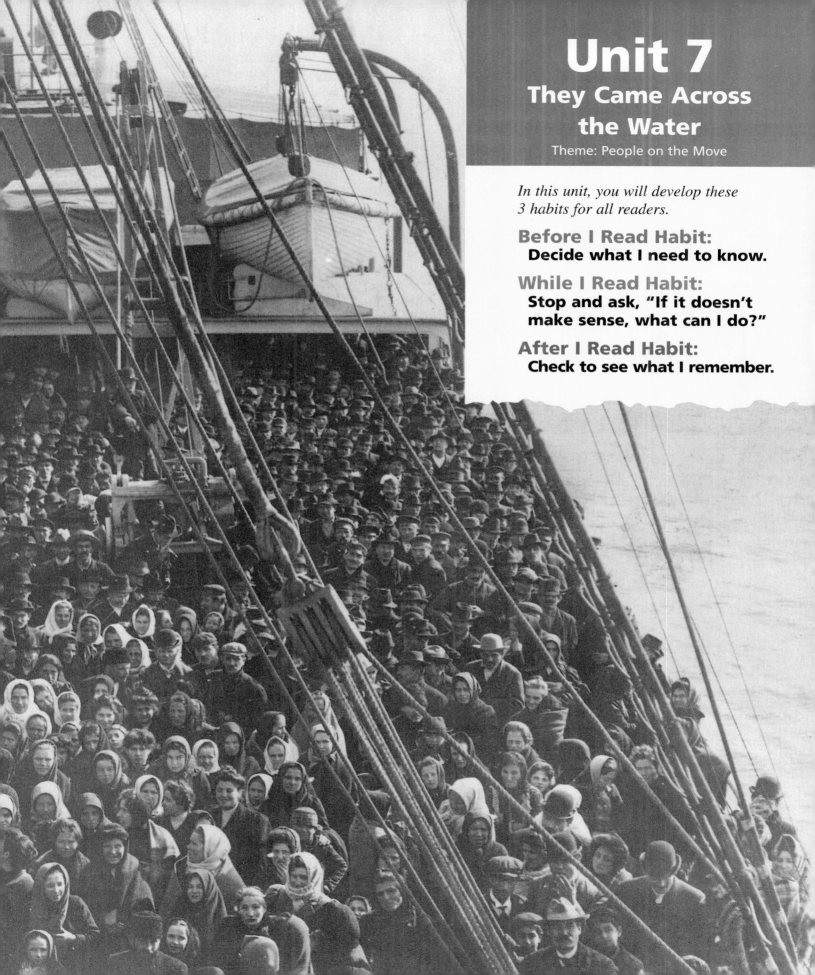

Unit 7
They Came Across the Water
Theme: People on the Move

In this unit, you will develop these 3 habits for all readers.

Before I Read Habit:
Decide what I need to know.

While I Read Habit:
Stop and ask, "If it doesn't make sense, what can I do?"

After I Read Habit:
Check to see what I remember.

Learn 3 of the 9 Habits

In this unit, you will develop three habits—one for before you read, one for while you are reading, and one for after you finish reading. Start with **Before I Read**. Read the habit and strategy. Then read my notes below.

Before I Read

Which **HABIT** will I learn?
> **Decide what I need to know.**
> If I develop this habit, I will have a reason for reading. I will understand it better and remember more of what I read.

Which **STRATEGY** will I use to learn this habit? Choose the features that best help me ask purpose-setting questions.

My Notes

- Strategy says to look at the selection and choose the features that help me ask purpose-setting questions. Features are things like heads, pictures, and captions.

- I can turn heads into questions and read to find the answers. I can do the same thing with pictures and captions, introductions and summaries, or boldfaced words.

- For this selection, I think I'll read the first and last paragraphs. They look like they have a lot of information.

- Here are some questions I can ask: Why did Dan Thuy leave Vietnam? Why did she come to California? What was life like in Thailand? What's different about Dan's new life in the United States?

- Now I have a purpose for reading.

Excerpts From
Dan Thuy's New Life in AMERICA

by Karen O'Connor

aspects (**as**·pekts)—ways to look at or think about something

Large grocery stores and shopping malls are familiar sights to most Americans. But to 13-year-old Dan Thuy Huynh (pronounced *Dahn Twee Hween*), these are among the many surprising **aspects** of life in the United States. Fast food, movie theaters, computers, and the English language are also new to Dan Thuy and her family since they moved from Vietnam to San Diego, California, after spending three years in Thailand [**tie**·land]. They have lived in the United States just four months.

Vietnam, Dan Thuy's homeland, is a small country in Southeast Asia about the size of California. It is located south of China between the South China Sea on the east and Laos and Cambodia (also called Kampuchea [kam·poo·**chee**·uh]) to the west.

The Huynh family (left to right): KimHong, Dan Tram, Gu Thanh, and Dan Thuy

Now read the habit and strategy for **While I Read**. When you see ❓, read my notes in the margin.

While I Read

Which **HABIT** will I learn?

Stop and ask, "If it doesn't make sense, what can I do?"
If I develop this habit, I will stop and figure out what to do so what I'm reading makes sense. Then I can keep reading and not be lost.

Which **STRATEGY** will I use to learn this habit?
Select the best strategy (context clues, word parts, dictionary) to help me understand words.

economic
(ek·uh·**nom**·ik)—having to do with the earning and managing of money

Dan Thuy and her family are immigrants—people who have moved permanently from one country to another. In some ways, immigrants lead a double life. They are caught between the old culture and the new, between their native language and a new language, between friends in the old place and friends in the new.

Immigrants have populated the United States throughout its history. Since the early 17th century, more than 50 million people from countries all over the world have left their homelands for the religious, political, and **economic** freedom that America offers. Between 1904 and 1914 alone, nearly one million immigrants a year poured into the country. Following waves of European immigration early in the 20th century, many Asian and Hispanic people have moved to America in recent decades.

When the Huynhs arrived in the United States, they had an advantage that many immigrants do not have. Several members of their family had come to America during the mid-1970s, so aunts, uncles, cousins, and grandparents were there to greet them.

Many Vietnamese immigrants settle in Southern California because the warm, mild climate is similar to that of their native land. Some choose the area because they know other Vietnamese people there. The sight of people from their homeland helps immigrants feel that they belong.

The family gathers for a meal.

This Sunday morning, Dan Thuy, her nine-year-old sister Dan Tram, and their parents, Gu Thanh and KimHong, visit relatives for **brunch**. Some members of the family leave their shoes at the door, following Vietnamese tradition. Others wear their shoes, preferring to follow the American custom.

Dan Thuy's uncle Nu is KimHong's brother. Nu and his wife Sau (known to her American friends as Sally) sponsored the Huynh family when they moved from Vietnam to the United States. A sponsor is a person or organization that agrees to help immigrants settle in the United States. The sponsor helps the immigrants find work and a place to live. Ten years ago, friends of Nu and Sau sponsored them and their five children when they came from Vietnam. Now it is Nu's turn to offer the same kind of help to his sister and her family. *Strategy Alert!*

• • •

As they sit around the table, some family members speak English. Others speak Vietnamese. Some of the younger people even mix the two languages in one sentence.

Mastering a new language is not easy. Dan Thuy and her parents say they have much to learn. Dan Thuy's mother, KimHong, practices her English every day at her job in a manicure salon. But she still feels uncertain about her language skills.

Dan Thuy also worries about her English. "I have many fears," she says, "because English is my second language. I am afraid people will not understand what I say when I speak or write."

Gu Thanh is not working right now because of a back injury, so he uses his time to attend English classes. "I am really busy," he says with a wide smile. "I have to study, take care of my children, and find a job. There are many things to do."

• • •

brunch—breakfast and lunch eaten as one meal late in the morning

Stop and Ask ❓

If it doesn't make sense, what can I do? Select the best strategy (context clues, word parts, dictionary) to help me understand words like *sponsored*.

I could look up *sponsored* in the dictionary. First I'll look for clues in the sentences around it. When I keep reading I see that the word is explained in the next sentence.

It says that people suffer persecution because of their race, religion, or political opinions. That's a context clue. I know that those are reasons that people are sometimes treated badly. Suffer also makes me think it's something bad. I think that *persecution* means "bad treatment."

regime (ray·**zheem**)— a system of rule or government

The Huynh family first began to study English during the three years they lived in a refugee [ref·yoo·**jee**] camp in Thailand. The United Nations defines refugees as "persons suffering persecution because of political opinion, membership in a particular social group, race, ethnicity, or religion." Refugees such as the Huynhs often leave their homeland because they fear death or imprisonment. **?** *Strategy Alert!*

In 1975, after the Vietnam War, Communist soldiers from North Vietnam took over South Vietnam. In April the southern city of Saigon fell to North Vietnamese troops. The city became a mass of frightened people desperate to get out before they were killed or imprisoned. Men, women, and children clogged the streets and jammed the airport runways. They tried to leave by any means they could.

After this first wave of refugees fled Vietnam in 1975, the rate of people leaving the country slowed down. Then, during the 1980s, a second wave of refugees left the country because of difficult living conditions. Unfortunately, after 1975, planes were not available to fly people out of the country. The only way out was by boat. Citizens who fled Vietnam in this way—perhaps as many as 370,000 of them—came to be known as *boat people*.

The boat people tell many stories about the horrors they experienced on their journey to freedom. Some of the boats were so overcrowded they fell apart. Others sank in storms and rough waters. Still others set sail in bad weather and spent days drifting in fog and rain with little water and food for the passengers. In addition, pirates attacked the boats, robbing and sometimes even killing people.

Nonetheless, refugees continued to pour out of Vietnam. To remain there under the Communist **regime** could mean death, working for the state, or losing one's family ties. To those who could leave, risking death in a boat was better than life in a land of hatred.

Like so many others, the Huynhs fled the Communist regime and escaped Vietnam by boat. It was a very difficult time for Gu Thanh and his family. . . .

But Gu Thanh knew he must try to leave. "In my country," he says, "we have a saying, 'Freedom or death.'" He and his family sailed to Thailand, where they could stay in a refugee camp until it was possible to move to the United States.

These refugees left Vietnam for Thailand on a crowded boat.

haven (**hay**·vuhn)—
a safe place

Refugees do construction work at a camp.

The first refugee camps were put together quickly during the mid-1970s to provide a **haven** for the thousands of refugees who were fleeing Vietnam, Laos, and Cambodia (Kampuchea). Most of the early camps were overcrowded and dirty and lacked adequate food, clothing, and medicine.

During the 1980s, however, many of the camps improved under the management of the United Nations High Commissioner for Refugees. In addition, international relief organizations such as the Red Cross, CARE, World Vision International, and others provided medical care, clothing, food, and education. *Strategy Alert!*

Despite the changes, life in the refugee camp was still hard for the Huynh family. There were no **luxuries** and few jobs. Worst of all was the boredom of having nothing to do. Children and teenagers tried to keep busy with school, crafts, and sports. Some adults ran small businesses or coffeehouses. Others used skills they had learned in their native country, such as cutting hair or tailoring.

But the refugees spent most of their time in the camp waiting—waiting for the day when all of the papers necessary for immigration would be completed. "We were in Thailand for three years," Gu Thanh says. "It felt like a jail."

Many things can slow down the immigration process. When a family like the Huynhs applies to move to the United States, an agent from the U.S. Immigration and Naturalization Service (INS) opens a file of information about the family. The file includes documents such as birth certificates and military records. Sometimes documents must be sent from Vietnam, which can take a long time. The waiting period also depends on the number of people who have applied to immigrate, the number of available immigration officers, and the time it takes to process the applications. *Strategy Alert!*

Stop and Ask

If it doesn't make sense, what can I do? Select the best strategy (context clues, word parts, dictionary) to help me understand words like *relief*.

• • • • • • • • • •

It says that the relief organizations gave things like medicine, food, and clothing. Those things help people. I think that relief means "help given to people who need it."

luxuries
(**lug**·zhoor·eez)—
anything that is more than what is absolutely necessary

Stop and Ask

If it doesn't make sense, what can I do? Select the best strategy (context clues, word parts, dictionary) to help me understand words like *documents*.

• • • • • • • • • •

It says "documents such as birth certificates and military records." I know that those things are important papers. Documents must mean "important papers."

If it doesn't make sense, what can I do? Select the best strategy (context clues, word parts, dictionary) to help me understand words like *stucco*.

○○○○○○○○○○

I can tell that this is a type of house, but there aren't any clues that help more than that. When I look this word up in the dictionary, it tells me that *stucco* is "plaster with a rough or wavy finish."

If it doesn't make sense, what can I do? Select the best strategy (context clues, word parts, dictionary) to help me understand words like *reunion*.

○○○○○○○○○○

I think I can use word parts to figure this out. I know that *union* means "something that is joined or united." I also know that the prefix *re-* means "again." So here, *reunion* must mean "people who are joined together again."

proverb (**prov**·urb)— a wise, old saying

The number of immigrants and refugees accepted into the United States varies year by year as immigration laws change. In 1988, for example, a total of 643,000 immigrants settled in the United States. Of these, 264,000 were from Asian countries, and 29,000 came from Vietnam.

Finally the day arrived when the papers for Gu Thanh and his family were ready. An INS agent interviewed them. After they were accepted as refugees, the INS arranged for them to travel to the United States, where their sponsors were waiting.

The Huynhs were lucky. They had family members who could pick them up at the airport, and they had a warm home to go to—the small, white stucco house in San Diego where KimHong's parents live. *? Strategy Alert!*

KimHong's father works in his garden.

For KimHong, the reunion with her mother and father and other members of her family made the hard journey to the United States worth it. Nonetheless, immigrating was a mixed blessing for both her and her husband, Gu Thanh. *? Strategy Alert!*

"We have a **proverb** in Vietnam," Gu Thanh says. " 'No place is better than my country.' I am happy to be here, and I don't worry about anything anymore, but I still have my parents, brothers, and sister in Vietnam. I miss them so much."

KimHong also has mixed feelings about the move. "In Vietnam, we lived under the Communist regime, so it was very difficult to get a job, hard to make money, and my children could not attend school," she reflects. "I like living in the United States with my family, but I think that if my country had not had the Communist regime, life would have been better there."

KimHong misses her native land. "I miss the fields," she says softly. She remembers the way they looked just after the **monsoon** season, with colored leaves falling from the trees, and the way the sun rose over the mountains. She does not like what Vietnam has become under Communist rule, but it is still her country, and she misses it—especially the Vietnam she knew as a girl.

Gu Thanh pauses to consider what his family has accomplished since leaving Vietnam. "We won," he says. "Now I think to myself, it was a terrible past. I want to forget everything that happened. I feel happy in this new country." He adds, "When you had a lot of things to survive, you do the best you can and you realize the value of life."

. . .

Dan Thuy is now beginning to feel at home in the United States. During her first days here, however, she was afraid. "I had trouble sleeping because the time wasn't the same, and everything I saw was different from my life in Thailand and Vietnam."

When Dan Thuy and her family arrived in San Diego, they needed help with communicating, grocery shopping, finding work, and enrolling in school. They had to learn how to open a bank account, how to use public transportation, and how to find their way around a strange city. Dan Thuy also encountered many unfamiliar items, such as a tube of toothpaste, a can opener, and a tape dispenser.

Immigrant children are often given a lot of responsibility in the new country. Because they usually learn the language faster than their parents, they are expected to act as translators—making doctor's appointments, answering the telephone, writing letters, and helping the adults read printed announcements, forms, and newspapers. *Strategy Alert!*

The challenges are less frightening for Dan Thuy now because she knows more English. Still, she is cautious. "I never go shopping alone," says Dan Thuy, "because I am afraid I would get lost."

. . . .

monsoon (mon•soon)— a seasonal wind that brings heavy rains to Asia

Stop and Ask ❓

If it doesn't make sense, what can I do? Select the best strategy (context clues, word parts, dictionary) to help me understand words like *translators*.

I know the prefix *trans-* means "across," and the text is talking about language here. I think *translators* must be people who go "across language"—like from another language into English.

One of Dan Thuy's chores is to hang her family's clothes out to dry.

Like many immigrant teenagers, Dan Thuy is learning English through a process called *total immersion*. That means she attends regular classes with the other students, practicing her English by listening and speaking in a variety of situations. She got an introduction to the language at the refugee camp, but there is still more to learn.

To increase her vocabulary, Dan Thuy goes to the school library and reads books in English. She also learns about her own culture at the public library. In an effort to serve the local immigrant population, one library in San Diego has enlarged its collection of Vietnamese books, information, and services. The Vietnamese materials include folklore, romance novels, information about United States citizenship, and instruction in English. (The Huynhs are not yet U.S. citizens. That will take about five years.)

Many inner-city schools in San Diego serve a large number of immigrants from Vietnam, Laos, Kampuchea, and China. Teachers at these schools make a point of **incorporating** Southeast Asian studies, festivals, and customs into their lesson plans.

Dan Thuy loves school. "I have a lot of friends there," she says, "and I like learning so much English."

· · ·

Dan Thuy holds a small doll that wears one of the hand-**crocheted** dresses she learned to make in the refugee camp. "I don't have time to crochet anymore," she says. She is too busy with school, sports, and friends.

"My dream is to continue studying and to attend college," she says. Before climbing into her bunk bed, Dan Thuy writes a letter to her grandparents in Vietnam, telling them about her new life in the United States.

Dan Thuy reads books in English to increase her vocabulary.

incorporating
(in·**kor**·puh·rayt·ing)—including as part of something else

crocheted
(kroh·**shayd**)—made of connecting loops of yarn by using a hooked needle

Congratulations! You finished reading. Now read the habit and strategy for **After I Read**. Then read my notes below.

After I Read

Which **HABIT** will I learn?

Check to see what I remember.

If I develop this habit, I will check to see what I remember as soon as I finish reading. It helps me see if I really understood what I read and helps me remember it better, too.

Which **STRATEGY** will I use to learn this habit?

Decide which features I should use to question myself about what I've read.

My Notes

• Strategy says to decide which features I should use to ask myself questions about what I remember.

• Let's see—I can use the heads to ask myself questions or I can use the pictures.

• I don't see any heads in this story, so I'll use the pictures and the captions to question myself.

• The picture on page 196 shows the boat people. Here's one question: Who were the boat people? That question can help me remember a lot about what I read.

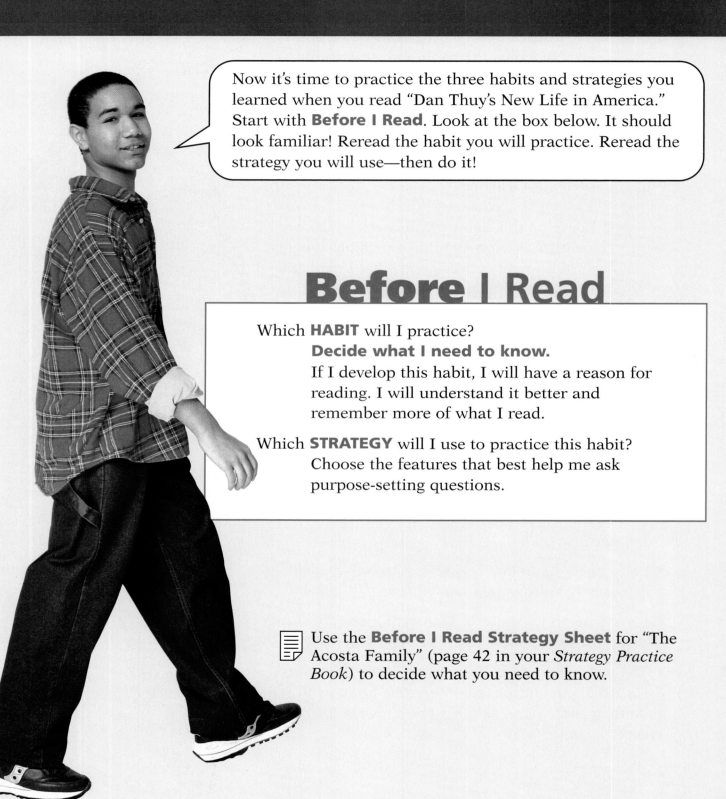

Now it's time to practice the three habits and strategies you learned when you read "Dan Thuy's New Life in America." Start with **Before I Read**. Look at the box below. It should look familiar! Reread the habit you will practice. Reread the strategy you will use—then do it!

Before I Read

Which **HABIT** will I practice?
Decide what I need to know.
If I develop this habit, I will have a reason for reading. I will understand it better and remember more of what I read.

Which **STRATEGY** will I use to practice this habit?
Choose the features that best help me ask purpose-setting questions.

Use the **Before I Read Strategy Sheet** for "The Acosta Family" (page 42 in your *Strategy Practice Book*) to decide what you need to know.

In The Mexican American Family Album, *Dorothy and Thomas Hoobler interview several Mexican Americans. The Hooblers wanted to learn about their experiences in the United States. In the following interview, the Hooblers talk with the Acosta family. The Acostas came to San Antonio, Texas, in 1920. They opened a shop called the Acosta Music Company. Over the years, three generations of Acostas have run the business, which is now headed by Mike Acosta. Refugia Acosta Alonso, Mike's aunt, was five years old when the family crossed the Rio Grande from Mexico. In the first passage, Refugia describes how the Mexican Revolution caused her family to flee their homeland.*

The Acosta Family

Excerpted From
The Mexican American Family Album
by Dorothy and Thomas Hoobler

TOP (from left):
Bernice Acosta-Cole,
Mike Acosta,
Michael Acosta, Jr.,
Belinda Acosta,
and Olga Acosta,
Mike's wife

BOTTOM: Guadelupe
Acosta in the family
music store, 1931

Refugia:

Because of the fighting, people tried to get out. People went hungry, even if they had money, because the government changed the money [issued new currency, making the old bills valueless]. Then my grandfather said, "I am going to get out of here," because at that time he belonged to the Estado Major [mah·**hor**], men of Pancho Villa [**vee**·ya]. And his oldest son was only 15, but the government was taking young men [into the Mexican army].

Reread the habit and strategy below. Look for the *Strategy Alerts!* as you continue to read.

While I Read

Which HABIT will I practice?

Stop and ask, "If it doesn't make sense, what can I do?"
If I develop this habit, I will stop and figure out what to do so what I'm reading makes sense. Then I can keep reading and not be lost.

Which STRATEGY will I use to practice this habit?
Select the best strategy (context clues, word parts, dictionary) to help me understand words.

Use the **While I Read Strategy Sheet** for "The Acosta Family" (page 43 in your *Strategy Practice Book*) as you read.

pulpit (**pul**·pit)—a raised platform used for preaching

Stop and Ask

If it doesn't make sense, what can I do? Select the best strategy (context clues, word parts, dictionary) to help me understand words like *revolution*.

We took a train, and we came to Nuevo Laredo [**nweh**·voh la·**ray**·doh] [Mexico] where the revolution* was already going on. And they had burned half of the bridge so that people couldn't come across. A lot of people had no place to go, and they were all over the city. They lived in shacks or tents that had been donated by the U.S. army. We lived there until the fighting stopped and then came across to Laredo [Texas], where we had a nice room. My daddy [Guadelupe] used to play in a band and also to make guitars. My brother and I used to help him. In Nuevo Laredo he made a communion rail and a **pulpit** for the church. I haven't been there for a long time, but it's still there. In fact the priest of the church was the godfather for [her brother] Miguel [mee·**gel**], who was born in Nuevo Laredo. *Strategy Alert!*

In 1920 we moved to San Antonio, because my grandmother, my mother's mother, was already here. Maybe you heard about the chili queens that used to live here in San Antonio way back in the old days. Over at the farmer's market, in the square. Well at that time, at about 4:30 in the morning old ladies used to sell chili there. My grandmother was one of them.

These people are eating food prepared at an outdoor plaza.

She would sell **menudo,** chili con carne [**kar**·nay], and tamales [tuh·**mah**·lees]. The Southern Pacific Railroad ran through here, and a lot of Mexican people worked on the tracks. They would get up at five or six o'clock and want something to eat. So that's where grandmother made her money. And by six or seven o'clock she had sold everything.

Q: Why did your father decide to start the music store?

Refugia:

Sí, he was a very independent man. He didn't like to work for anybody. He had made the **bajo sexto** in Mexico with my grandfather, and by the time he came here he was skilled. He was a perfectionist.* He had a special place where he would get the wood. He was very careful, picked out just the right kind. *Strategy Alert!*

At that time everything was done by hand, no machines. A typical day, he would start in the morning by eight, seven-thirty. Sometimes people would want a guitar quickly, and he would work hard till nine o'clock at night.

But when he decided to start his business, it was a sacrifice for all of us. Nowadays, you have Christmas, kids have a tree, get all kinds of presents. The next day they throw it away, because they get too much. On our Christmas, my daddy would say to my mother, "What do the children need?" And she would say this one needs shoes, that one needs a coat. And we were satisfied with that, because we needed it.

Outside of that we used to have a lot of food. Tamales, buñuelos [buh·**nway**·lohs], champurals.* You make champurals with masa [corn meal], add some water to it, then strain it and put in some cinnamon and sugar. Then you toast it until it becomes thick like warm, creamy cereal. It was a hot meal and that was good to eat in the winter. So we used to have a lot of that, because my grandmother would make a lot of good things. *Strategy Alert!*

menudo (muh·**noo**·doh)—a soup made with tripe, the lining of a cow's stomach

bajo sexto (**bah**·hoh **seks**·toh)—a 12-string bass guitar

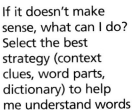

Stop and Ask

If it doesn't make sense, what can I do? Select the best strategy (context clues, word parts, dictionary) to help me understand words like *perfectionist.*

Stop and Ask

If it doesn't make sense, what can I do? Select the best strategy (context clues, word parts, dictionary) to help me understand words like *champurals.*

Miguel (left), Guadelupe (above left), and Luis (above right) show some of the steps in making a guitar.

Three of Guadelupe Acosta's sons joined the family business, and it became the largest musical instrument company in San Antonio during the 1930s and 1940s. Miguel Acosta, the youngest son, became widely known for the quality of guitars he made, and he often used them to perform in public. Miguel's oldest son, Mike, keeps the Acosta Music Company going today.

Q: When did you join the family business?

Mike:

I started in the shop in 1956, when I was in high school. Because of the music that was popular at that time, there was a big demand for guitars. My father had pretty much closed down, but then I started things again. But I just run the shop in the evenings now, repairing guitars, violins, other instruments. The guitars you see hanging on the wall are rebuilt and repaired ones—not handmade.

The business **thrived** in the 1930s and 1940s. Back then, they had a print shop where they printed their own songbooks as well. All of us kids used to do the binding and folding at night, after school. The books were sold all over the country, wherever there was a Mexican community.

At that time my father could sell a handmade guitar for about $145. But you couldn't make a living doing that now. With machine-made guitars available, you couldn't charge enough for the work of a handmade one.

thrived—grew and did very well

Q: This picture shows a double-neck guitar that your father made in 1947. How did he get the idea for it?

Mike:

Well, after he came back from serving in World War II, in 1945, he used to play with some local bands. And whenever they didn't have a bass player, or couldn't afford one, he had to play a bajo sexto, a 12-string bass guitar. So as a guitar-maker, he came up with the idea of a double-neck guitar. It was a combination of a regular six-string and a bajo sexto. Unfortunately, he never did **patent** his idea. And in 1947, he used it with an electric amplifier as well. It was practical and made sense, because he didn't have to carry two guitars. Later the big guitar manufacturers came out with the same thing, but he was the first to develop it.

Q: What was it like to grow up in San Antonio? Did you ever experience prejudice?

Mike:

I don't know if you can call it prejudice, but there weren't very many advantages for Mexican Americans in our school. Mostly our school was a vocational* school. There weren't many college preparatory courses. They trained you for carpentry, painting, stuff like that. *Strategy Alert!*

At one time I worked for a pharmacy and I wanted to save money to enter pharmacy school. I went to the dean's office, and they told me that was a waste of time—that I was supposed to be a carpenter, and I had to take carpentry courses, graduate from high school and get a job to help my parents. There was no encouragement to take college courses.

patent (pat·nt)—
a government document that protects an invention from being made or sold by anyone besides the inventor

Stop and Ask ?

If it doesn't make sense, what can I do? Select the best strategy (context clues, word parts, dictionary) to help me understand words like *vocational.*

Q: What about your children? Have they lost a sense of their Mexican Spanish heritage?

Mike:

Yes. I don't think nowadays kids care so much about it. They're more interested in getting ahead, making money, having a better life-style. My kids didn't have it as hard as we did.

Mike's children—Bernice, Belinda, and Michael, Jr.—the fourth generation of Acostas in the United States—describe their own experiences.

Bernice:

Well, one thing about San Antonio is that even though it is the tenth-largest city in the nation it still has that small-town feel to it. When I go to visit friends in Houston and Dallas, those cities are kind of over-whelming. And San Antonio has the Spanish influence and culture. All the festivities* like fiesta [fee•**es**•tah], the block festivals, the architecture, the music—are Hispanic. ❓ *Strategy Alert!*

Stop and Ask ❓

If it doesn't make sense, what can I do? Select the best strategy (context clues, word parts, dictionary) to help me understand words like *festivities.*

The River Walk in San Antonio, Texas, is lighted at Christmastime.

Belinda:

Growing up in San Antonio, one thing I remember is the influence of the Catholic community. I spent the last two years of my high school education in public schools and that was the first time I ever met Protestants or Jews. I think the reason is that most of the festivities in San Antonio just surround the Catholic community—**parish** festivals. The greatest cultural influence in the city is Catholic, and most people are involved in them.

Michael, Jr.:

One thing that I remember about the family is the closeness. Even when I lived in different parts of the country, I found that Hispanic families seem to be close. And even if you're not part of the family, other Hispanics seem to welcome you in and treat you like their own, which I think is a very important part of the culture.

One of the things I remember that I still enjoy are family gatherings. I can't count all the times we've gotten together for Christmas or Easter or someone's birthday. We're talking about 20, 30, or 40 people just sitting down and eating and drinking and celebrating. I think that's what being Hispanic is all about—family. I think another part is the Church, which has been an important part of my life. I've been an **altar boy**. I was in a Christian music group in high school, attended Catholic school. And I think it's a meeting place that is part of our culture.

Q: Do you think you will carry on these traditions with your own family?

Michael, Jr.:

I think I will. I think it's very important. Today, with all the violence, I think family values are important to instill in our children. I'm getting married in November and I think it's very healthy to be family oriented.

Mission San Jose in San Antonio, Texas

parish (par·ish)—all the people who worship at one church

altar boy—a boy who assists the clergy during a church service

If it doesn't make sense, what can I do? Select the best strategy (context clues, word parts, dictionary) to help me understand words like *hyphenate*.

Q: Bernice, when you got married, you kept the name Acosta. Sometimes you hyphenate* it with your husband's name, Acosta-Cole. Why is that? ❓ *Strategy Alert!*

Bernice:

Well, marrying a non-Hispanic as well as a non-Catholic, I feel that it's important that my children are aware of their background. They will be exposed to both cultures, both traditions, and I want them to enjoy and appreciate the Hispanic culture as well as their other culture.

Bernice Acosta-Cole's desire to carry on Mexican traditions is a feeling expressed by many of the people interviewed for The Mexican American Family Album. *Although parents want their children to feel comfortable in American culture, they also try hard to pass on their own traditions.*

One of the traditions honored by many Mexican Americans is remembering the Day of the Dead. In early November, Mexicans and Mexican Americans hold special celebrations to remember loved ones who have died. People set candles in the cemetery where their loved ones are buried. They create archways out of flowers. The arches are said to allow the souls of friends and relatives to return for a social visit.

Day of the Dead festivities include visiting cemeteries (left), making papier mâché figures (top), and decorating gravesites (bottom).

Now that you've finished reading, review the **After I Read** habit below. Think about what you read in "The Acosta Family" as you practice the strategy.

After I Read

Which **HABIT** will I practice?

Check to see what I remember.

If I develop this habit, I will check to see what I remember as soon as I finish reading. It helps me see if I really understood what I read and helps me remember it better, too.

Which **STRATEGY** will I use to practice this habit?

Decide which features I should use to question myself about what I've read.

 Use the **After I Read Strategy Sheet** for "The Acosta Family" (page 44 in your *Strategy Practice Book*) to see what you remember.

Now read "One More Border" and apply these three habits and strategies.

Before I Read

Which **HABIT** will I apply?
Decide what I need to know.

Which **STRATEGY** will I use to apply this habit?
Choose the features that best help me ask purpose-setting questions.

While I Read

Which **HABIT** will I apply?
Stop and ask, "If it doesn't make sense, what can I do?"

Which **STRATEGY** will I use to apply this habit?
Select the best strategy (context clues, word parts, dictionary) to help me understand words.

After I Read

Which **HABIT** will I apply?
Check to see what I remember.

Which **STRATEGY** will I use to apply this habit?
Decide which features I should use to question myself about what I've read.

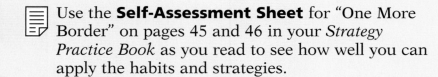

Use the **Self-Assessment Sheet** for "One More Border" on pages 45 and 46 in your *Strategy Practice Book* as you read to see how well you can apply the habits and strategies.

Excerpted From
One More Border

The True Story of One Family's Escape From War-Torn Europe

by William Kaplan with Shelley Tanaka

"Nomi," Igor [**ee**·gor] whispered, shaking his sister awake. "Get up!"

Nomi rolled over and rubbed her eyes. Her brother was dressed in his good trousers and jacket, the ones he wore to synagogue [**sin**·uh·gog]. Behind him, Mother and Father hurried past the door carrying clothes and large suitcases.

"I don't want to get up," Nomi said. "It's too early."

"But we have to leave Memel [**may**·muhl]," Igor insisted, pulling at the blankets. "The Nazis [**naht**·seez] are coming to the city and they hate Jews."

"Why?" Nomi looked up at her older brother. Igor was tall and thin and very smart. He knew everything.

But this time he just shook his head. "I don't know. But we have to go."

The Kaplans (left to right): Igor, Mother (Nadja), Nomi, and Father (Bernard)

These people were required to wear a star on their clothing to identify them as Jewish.

Nomi thought it was almost like being on holiday. But Igor heard his parents whispering late at night. He saw how his mother picked at her food, how Father stopped giving them money for candies in the hotel shop.

Then, in the fall, Germany invaded Poland, Lithuania's neighbor to the south. By the following summer, Russian troops had moved into Lithuania [lith•oo•**ay**•nee•uh] from the east, to protect their own frontier, they said.

Igor and Nomi stopped going to school. Igor saw letters arriving from Canada, where his grandparents had moved a few years before.

"Are we going to live in the hotel forever?" he asked his father. "Why aren't we going to school?"

"Russia controls Lithuania now," Father said. "They don't like the Jews any more than the Nazis do. They've closed our schools and synagogues and made it difficult for Jews to be Jews."

"Where can we go and still be Jews?"

His father put a hand on his shoulder. "We are going to try to go to Canada, where Oma and Opa live."

"Is Canada far?" Nomi asked.

"Yes," Father sighed. "Very, very far."

Igor peered at the large map lying on the table in the hotel room. Each country was outlined in pale colors crisscrossed with black lines that showed the roads and railroads. Lithuania was a tiny yellow blob bordering the Baltic Sea. But the biggest expanse belonged to Russia, its pink borders stretching east all the way to the Sea of Japan and the Pacific Ocean.

Father had explained that going to Canada would not be easy. All over Europe, borders were shutting down as more and more countries joined the war. The Kaplans needed written permission to leave Lithuania, but no one would give them these visas [**vee**·zuhz]. Without them, they were trapped in their own country, and time was running out.

Then, in late August, Father burst into the hotel room, and this time his face was full of hope.

"There is a Japanese consul here in Kaunas. His name is Sugihara [soo·gi·hah·rah]. They say he has been giving Jews transit visas to leave Russia and enter Japan."

Father grasped Igor's shoulder and squeezed it hard.

"Maybe Mr. Sugihara can help us, too," he said.

Igor's heart sank as he trudged up the hill to the Japanese consulate. Hundreds of people were clustered outside the black iron fence surrounding the white house. Father said that many of these people had been waiting for weeks, hoping to get a visa from Mr. Sugihara.

Across from the consulate was a park. As they passed it, Igor noticed a sign posted on the fence: **NO JEWS ALLOWED.**

Just then, at the side of the house, a gate opened, and a large black car drove out. The car moved slowly past the Kaplan family. It was driven by a weary-looking Japanese man.

"Stop!" Igor's father shouted, and he ran after the car. He caught up and banged on the window. The man rolled it down. It was Mr. Sugihara.

"Please," Bernard Kaplan begged, and he held out a form.

"My government has ordered me to issue no more visas," Mr. Sugihara said. Then he noticed Igor and Nomi. They were gripping Mother's hand. He looked into the back seat, where two small boys sat quietly. The car was packed with suitcases and boxes. The Sugiharas were leaving.

Mr. Sugihara, Japanese consul in Kaunas, and his family

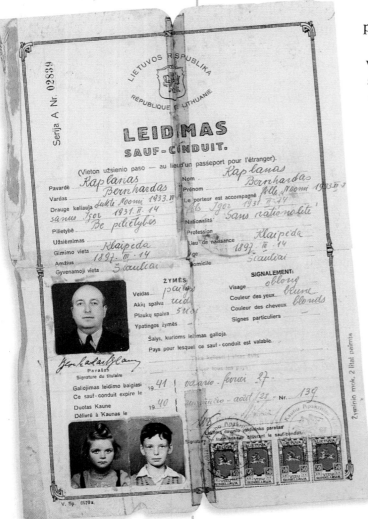

The visa that allowed Bernard, Igor, and Nomi Kaplan to escape Lithuania

Mr. Sugihara wrote something on the form, then pulled out a bright red stamp and stamped the paper.

"Good-bye," he nodded, and he rolled up the window. As the car disappeared down the street, Igor saw the faces of the boys pressed against the back window.

Igor hurriedly packed his bag as soon as they returned to the hotel. He was anxious [**angk**•shus] to leave.

But his parents huddled around the table, talking quietly. They sent Nomi to bed.

Igor couldn't understand it. They had their papers now. Hitler's troops were getting closer. Why were they waiting?

Then Father explained. The papers were only good for him and the two children, who traveled on their father's passport. But Mother was Russian. She needed separate permission to leave Lithuania.

Day after day she tried to get a visa from the Russian consulate. But the answer was always no. "Why would you want to leave?" the official would ask.

Two weeks passed. Igor saw the black headlines at the newsstand. The German troops were advancing.

Finally they could wait no longer.

"You must go without me," Mother said. Nomi began to cry. Mother bent down to give her a hug. "I won't give up," she promised. "I'm going back to the consulate. As soon as I get my papers, I'll follow you." But when Igor kissed his mother good-bye, she hugged him so hard that he could scarcely breathe. And he was suddenly afraid that he might never see her again.

The next afternoon, Igor, Nomi, and Father were at the Kaunas train station. They loaded their bags and then stood on the platform and waited. The engine blew a blast of steam. The conductor waved at them impatiently. They would have to get on board.

On the train, Igor stopped in the corridor while impatient passengers tried to squeeze by behind him. He pressed against the window, looking down the platform. The crowds had thinned.

The whistle blew. The steam cleared.

A woman ran down the platform, waving a paper in her hand.

"There she is!" he shouted. It was Mother.

The train lurched out of the station. Igor and Nomi leaned against Mother and watched the countryside slip by. Mother and Father sat quietly. Igor knew they were still worried. Mother's papers only allowed her to leave Lithuania. In Russia she would have to go to the Japanese embassy to try to get permission to enter Japan with the rest of the family.

Before long the train came to a stop. Igor pulled out his map and ran his finger along the line that marked the railway. They were at the border between Lithuania and Russia.

An officer opened the door.

"Papers," he demanded.

Father took out their papers and the officer examined them carefully. Igor could hear his mother's heart beating. She was very still.

The man looked at the papers for a long time. Then he handed them back. Other officials made them open their luggage. Some of the suitcases contained Mother's amber jewelry and family photographs in silver frames. The officials took those suitcases away.

"You can pick them up in Moscow," they said.

It was night when they arrived in Moscow. Mother went straight to the station master.

"Where are our missing suitcases?" she asked.

But the station master only laughed.

The next morning, Igor, Nomi, and Father toured Moscow, the capital of Russia. On Igor's map the city was just a round dot, like the center of a wheel where the spokes of roads and railways met. But it was the biggest city he had ever seen, its buildings and squares grand and imposing.

They walked down the vast parade ground of Red Square. They admired St. Basil's Cathedral sitting at one end of the square like a shining pink fairy castle. They walked around the walls of the Kremlin, Moscow's old fortress.

The Kremlin

• • •

All day Igor thought of his mother at the Japanese embassy. He imagined her seeing a gentle man like Mr. Sugihara, who would sign her papers with a few quick brush strokes and press on the bright red stamp.

But when they met her back at the train station, she was empty-handed.

"The emperor of Japan has ordered no more visas," she said. "The officials here are not like Mr. Sugihara. They are not prepared to disobey their government."

The Trans-Siberian Express just before it pulled out of Moscow

The trainman leaned out of the car and waved his yellow flag. The Trans-Siberian Express, the train that would take them to the other end of Russia, was ready to leave.

"We cannot wait," said Father. "We have tickets for this train. We must get as far as we can and hope for the best."

Igor had never been on a train like the Trans-Siberian Express. The family had their own compartment—a small room with seats that turned into bunk beds at night.

Igor spent hours with his nose pressed against the train window, watching the countryside slide by. At first the land was flat and covered with trees. Every so often a village appeared. Igor saw farmers eating their lunch in the middle of a field, their bread and soup bowls spread out on a blanket.

After two days, the mountains appeared. On Igor's map they looked like a long snake. Then everything became flat again, and even the people looked different.

"Why does everyone look so strange?" Nomi asked.

"The Ural [**yoor**·uhl] Mountains are the dividing line between Europe and Asia," Father explained. "We are now in Asia, so the people are Asian."

· · ·

Igor lost track of the days. Rosh Hashanah and Yom Kippur came and went. There was no celebration.

"Will we be safe when we get to the sea?" Nomi asked. She was sucking her thumb and lying on the seat staring at the ceiling. She wasn't terribly interested in the view.

Igor shook his head. "I don't know," he said. "The war is everywhere."

The nights suddenly grew very cold, and the forests were tinged with frost. On his map, Igor could see that the train was headed almost straight north. Then the track curved to the south, following a wide river with thick wooded hills on the other side. Beyond those hills lay China.

Igor leaned his forehead against the train window. They were almost at the end of the line. Soon, Father said, they would be able to smell the sea.

Igor watched the trees flash by. Birches, cedars, oaks . . . .

His eyes opened wide. Ahead, in the water on the far side of the river, he saw a large, pale shape. It was a tiger, standing in the brown water up to its belly, its coat long and thick, its eyes yellow and unblinking.

It was gone so quickly, Igor almost thought he had imagined it.

· · ·

Vladivostok [**vlad**·uh·**vos**·**tok**] was cold and crowded. Igor stayed very close to his father as he and Nomi followed him through the streets. They met Mother outside the Japanese consulate. Nomi rushed into her arms, but Mother barely seemed to see her. She just looked straight into Father's eyes and shook her head. She had been refused her visa.

Mother and Father moved to the side of the steps and talked quietly. Father reached into his coat and pulled out an envelope. Mother shook her head and began to cry. He pressed it into her hands. Mother looked at Igor and Nomi for a long time. Then she put the envelope in her pocket and went back into the consulate.

· · ·

Igor knew what the envelope contained. It was their money, the money for their new life in Canada.

He sat down on the steps. Nomi collected colorful leaves off the streets, but Igor felt frozen inside.

What would happen if the officials took the money and still didn't give Mother her visa? He knew such things happened.

He looked around at Vladivostok, hemmed in by dark hills and the icy harbor. Naval vessels, tugboats, and whaling ships crowded the stone piers. The air was filled with the sharp smell of seaweed and sawdust and the sounds of many languages that Igor had never heard before—Japanese, Korean, Chinese. Sailors, fishermen, and dock workers milled in the narrow streets. He saw no other children.

It was the most unfriendly city Igor had ever seen. How could they stay here? Where else could they go? They had reached the very end of the continent. Only the sea lay in front of them.

Rosh Hashanah
(rohsh hah·**shah**·nah)—the Jewish New Year (celebrated in early autumn)

Yom Kippur
(yohm kee·**poor**)—a Jewish holy day celebrated in early autumn

Father and Nomi sat down beside him. A cold wind began to blow down from the hills. Igor curled up against his father and fell asleep. He hadn't done that since he was little.

It was almost dark when Mother came out of the building. She was smiling wearily. She had her visa, and they were all finally free to leave Russia. But the envelope with the money was gone and, later, Igor noticed that his mother was no longer wearing her wedding ring.

"Eat," Mother said, pointing to the tray on the low table. "You must get your strength back after being so ill."

They were in a small inn in Kobe [**koh**·bee], Japan, waiting for their ship to leave for Canada. They had boarded a tramp steamer in Vladivostok, and the crossing to Japan had been crowded and noisy. The trip took several days longer than usual because of the stormy weather. Igor could still feel the lurching rise and fall of the boat. He'd been seasick for the whole trip.

He pushed a few grains of rice into his mouth. The food was so strange—rice and raw fish and smelly, bright yellow pickles. The tea tasted funny. There were no forks or spoons. The cups had no handles.

He shoved his bowl away. The delicate porcelain tipped on its tiny base and slipped to the floor and broke.

Father looked at Igor sternly, but he was too tired himself to be angry. Igor stared at the floor so Nomi wouldn't see his tears.

The *Empress of Russia* looked dressed for war, Igor thought. The ship sat in Kobe harbor, her long hull painted with ugly zigzagged stripes. She was even fitted with guns. Inside, however, she was still a passenger liner, with cabins and dining rooms.

Kobe, Japan, 1940s

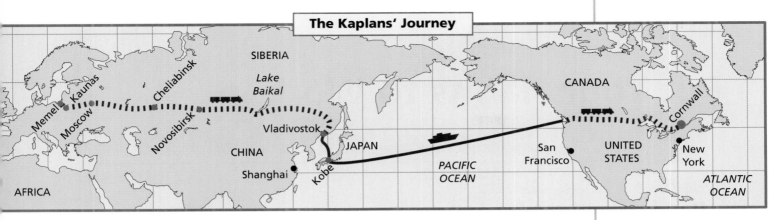

Map of the trip from Memel, Lithuania, to Cornwall, Canada

The voyage to Canada took seven days. Igor hated it. There was nothing to do, and Mother and Father had no money left for treats. There were no cities to look for on his map, no rivers or mountains to mark their route.

Vancouver [van·**koo**·vuhr] shimmered like a jewel in the October sunlight. Whitecapped mountains rose up behind the city.

"Papers, please."

Out of habit Igor stiffened when the immigration officer came on board and asked to see their documents. They were tattered from being folded and pulled out so many times.

He held his breath while the officer scanned the papers carefully, looking at each of their faces in turn. Igor wondered whether he still looked anything like the solemn boy in the photo on his father's passport. He felt as if he had left that boy far behind in the turret house in Memel.

Like a hammer the official stamp came down on the passport. The immigration officer waved the family through.

"Welcome to Canada," he said, smiling.

EPILOGUE

Igor Kaplan and his family settled on an abandoned farm just outside Cornwall, Ontario. It was a condition of their immigration that they spend at least a year working the land, but they had never farmed before, and they knew nothing about growing crops or raising livestock. Igor and Nomi went to the local school and learned to speak English in three months.

After a year, the family moved to Windsor, Ontario, where Nadja Kaplan opened a photography studio and the family began a new life. There were some difficult times ahead for the Kaplans, but overall the family prospered in Canada, a country they quickly came to love. Igor became a lawyer. Nomi became an artist.

As the war continued in Europe, they learned that they were among the last Jews to escape through Russia and Japan. By the time World War II was over in 1945, six million Jews had died in the Holocaust.

TOP: The Kaplan farmhouse in Canada

BOTTOM: Oma Kaplan with her chickens

Put Your Habits to Work in

Literature	Social Studies	Science	Math

Before I Read Habit:
Decide what I need to know.

Remember to decide what you need to know before you read a chapter in your social studies textbook. One way you can do that is to pick features to help you ask purpose-setting questions.

While I Read Habit:
Stop and ask, "If it doesn't make sense, what can I do?"

When you read your social studies book, stop if you come across a word you don't know. Then decide whether you should use word parts, other words in the sentence, or a dictionary to figure out what it means.

After I Read Habit:
Check to see what I remember.

When you're reading a social studies book, you're not finished until you check to see what you remember. You can do that by making up questions to check what you remember.

I'll use the pictures to write questions . . .

You may wish to use the **Put Your Habits to Work Sheet** (page 47 in your *Strategy Practice Book*) to practice these habits in your other reading.

Unit 8
The Future
Theme: Imagination

In this unit, you will develop these 3 habits for all readers.

Before I Read Habit:
Think about what I know about the subject.

While I Read Habit:
Stop and ask, "How does it connect to what I know?"

After I Read Habit:
React to what I've read.

Learn 3 of the 9 Habits

In this unit, you will develop three habits—one for before you read, one for while you are reading, and one for after you finish reading. Start with **Before I Read**. Read the habit and strategy. Then read my notes below.

Before I Read

Which **HABIT** will I learn?

Think about what I know about the subject.
If I develop this habit, I will bring to mind what I already know about the subject. This gets me ready to connect what I read to what I know so I will understand it better.

Which **STRATEGY** will I use to learn this habit?
Look at graphic aids, photos, and their captions to decide what I know about the subject.

My Notes

- Strategy says to look at the graphic aids, photos, and their captions to decide what I know about the subject of this article.

- A time line is a graphic aid. I see a time line on page 231.

- The time line mentions the Wright brothers. I know they flew an early airplane.

- The Model T is on the time line. I know that was a car and Henry Ford built it. I see a picture of Henry Ford.

- There's a diagram of an engine. I've seen an engine in our car.

- One caption is about magnetic trains. I know how magnets work but not how they could move trains.

From the Horse to the *Skycar*

A triumphal parade in ancient Rome

Imagine that a Roman soldier from the time of **Julius Caesar** had been frozen in time and was defrosted in the year 1800. He would have had no trouble getting around. Back then, and for thousands of years before, horses were the most common means of transportation.

In fact, there were very few changes in transportation in the 6,000-or-so years since humans **domesticated** horses. Better saddles and smoother carriages were developed. But in general, horses were still everywhere in 1800. They pulled carriages, plows, **streetcars,** and, of course, people. Horses were the main method of transportation in ancient Roman times, and they were still the main method in 1800. In that way, at least, the Roman soldier would have felt at home in 1800.

Julius Caesar (jool·yuhs **see·**zuhr)—one of ancient Rome's greatest rulers and generals, killed in 44 B.C.

domesticated (duh·**mes·**ti·kay·tid)— trained to be useful to people

streetcars (street·kahrz)—cars that move on rails in the street; trolleys

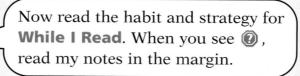

Now read the habit and strategy for **While I Read**. When you see , read my notes in the margin.

While I Read

Which **HABIT** will I learn?

Stop and ask, "How does it connect to what I know?"
If I develop this habit, I will think about how what I'm reading fits with what I know. This helps me understand the new material and remember it better.

Which **STRATEGY** will I use to learn this habit?
Decide whether I agree with what I am reading.

---

self-propelled (self-pruh•**peld**)—moves by its own power

 **Stop and Ask**

How does it connect to what I know? Decide whether I agree with what I am reading.

It says the Roman soldier could have gotten around in 1900. I never thought of that, but it's true. Riding a horse couldn't have changed very much!

Now imagine that the Roman soldier has just woken up today. Everything has changed! In many countries, horses are used solely for recreation and sports. People get around inside **self-propelled** metal boxes. They soar overhead in huge metal birds. Our Roman would be confused and frightened. Even if he knew where he was going, he couldn't get there without help.

The "Horseless Carriage"

If our imaginary Roman soldier had woken up sometime between 1800 and today—say in the year 1900—he could have gotten around. Although people were using railroads, electric streetcars, and powered ships for transportation, there were still plenty of horses. Few people owned the new and strange machines called *automobiles*. Most laughed at these noisy, smoky "horseless carriages." And then Henry Ford came along. *Strategy Alert!*

In 1908, Henry Ford's Model T, the "Tin Lizzie," sold for $850. By 1925, the price was lowered to $300, putting the car within reach of an average family. Ford joked that the Model T came in any color you wanted—as long as you wanted black! People didn't seem to mind. By 1928, more than 15 million Model Ts had been built. The automobile was here to stay.

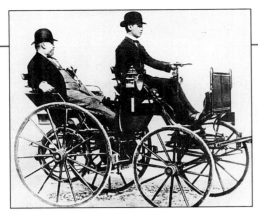

Gottlieb Daimler, German pioneer automobile manufacturer, in his first car

Henry Ford in 1896 with the first Ford automobile

But Ford had not invented cars. The first automobile was built in 1885 by German inventors Gottlieb Daimler [**got**·leeb **diem**·luhr] and Karl Benz. Their vehicle looked more like a high-wheeled tricycle than a car. The first popular car in America appeared in 1906. It was built by Ransom Olds, who called his machine the Oldsmobile.

The Age of the Automobile

Perhaps more than any other invention of the twentieth century, the car changed the way Americans lived. Around 1900, most people rarely traveled more than a few miles from their homes. Outside the cities, there were few paved roads. Long-distance travel by horse-drawn carriage was bumpy and uncomfortable. Trains were available, but they cost too much to use very often.

By the 1950s, however, families thought nothing of taking weekend trips of 100 miles or more. Millions of people had moved from the cities into the suburbs. They drove back and forth to work every day. New things appeared, such as parking lots, garages, drive-in theaters, drive-in restaurants, shopping malls, and mini-marts. All of these changes resulted from the fact that people were getting around in their cars. *Strategy Alert!*

During Henry Ford's time, Americans traveled an average of 340 miles a year by car. By the late 1960s, that number had grown to 10,000 miles a year!

Problems and Changes

Not all changes brought about by cars have been good. **Exhausts** from car engines have caused **smog** alerts. The great increase in the number of cars has caused traffic jams. Waterways have become polluted by oil spills. Supplies of gasoline have sometimes run short. Worst of all, the number of people killed in car accidents has grown. By the mid-1960s, more than 50,000 deaths per year in the United States were the result of auto accidents.

Stop and Ask ?

How does it connect to what I know? Decide whether I agree with what I am reading.

It says that the car changed the way Americans lived more than any other invention of the 20th century. I don't agree. Cars did change things. But I think computers have had a bigger effect than cars.

exhausts (ig·**zawsts**)— fumes or gases released from an engine

smog—fog polluted with smoke

Meanwhile, cars have changed. Just over a hundred years ago, a car was really a gasoline-powered tricycle. These days, it's a computer-controlled, air-conditioned, CD-blasting, telephone-equipped sport-utility vehicle [**vee**·i·kuhl]. *Strategy Alert!*

Cars and Computers

The greatest change in cars over the last 15 years has been the use of computers. Computers and **sensors** make the car safer, cleaner, and more **efficient**. In today's "smart car," sensors on the brakes can tell whether the road is slippery. Onboard computers "remember" how drivers position their seats and mirrors. Satellite **receivers** can help a lost driver locate a destination.

Computers also help the car run better in other ways. They control how the fuel is burned. They also adjust the shock absorbers if the road changes from smooth to bumpy. They maintain a steady temperature inside to keep the driver and passengers comfortable. Some computers even help drivers steer!

Auto engineers use computers to design safer seat belts and to improve air bags. When a vehicle hits something, a small explosive charge fires the air bag. It fills with air in less than one tenth of a second—faster than you can blink your eye. The driver's head and body hit the air bag instead of the steering wheel or the dashboard. When air bags and seat belts are used properly, they can save lives.

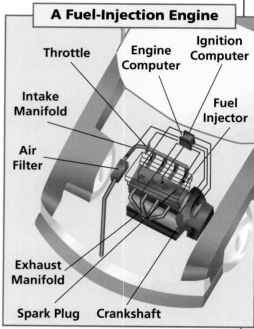

A Fuel-Injection Engine

Throttle, Engine Computer, Ignition Computer, Intake Manifold, Air Filter, Fuel Injector, Exhaust Manifold, Spark Plug, Crankshaft

Two computers control this four-cylinder fuel-injection engine.

The Road Ahead

No matter how many safety devices are put in cars, there's still one imperfect part that will continue to cause crashes—the driver! That's why auto engineers have long dreamed of a car with no driver. It would be a vehicle guided entirely by computers.

As our highways grow more crowded, there is less space between vehicles. So there is less time for drivers to make decisions that prevent crashes. But in the future, computers will make those decisions. For example, if one vehicle suddenly slows down, sensors in the vehicles will detect the change right away. The vehicles would automatically keep their distance from one another.

Stop and Ask ?

How does it connect to what I know? Decide whether I agree with what I am reading.

· · · · · · · · · · · · · ·

I'm not sure I agree. Not all cars are "air-conditioned, CD-blasting, telephone-equipped sport utility vehicles." There are also cars that are pretty fuel-efficient and don't pollute as badly as the older models.

sensors (**sen**·suhrz)— devices that respond to a signal

efficient (i·**fish**·uhnt)— effective with little waste

receivers (ri·**see**·vuhrz)— devices that pick up electric waves

In the future, computers will control vehicles even on uncrowded highways. They will act as **automatic** pilots. Cars will stay in the proper lanes by picking up signals from magnets in the roadway. The computers will control speed and steering. Drivers will only have to let the computers know where they want to go, and the computers will take them there!

❓ *Strategy Alert!*

Volts Instead of Gas?

Better computers won't be the only big change in the vehicles of the future. How vehicles get their power will change as well. In 10 or 20 years, you might be driving a "roadway-powered electric vehicle," which uses electricity instead of gasoline! Actually, this idea was first suggested over 100 years ago by a man named E. E. Ries.

The future version would be like a "personal streetcar." An electric cable would run through a tiny open tunnel a few feet under the roadway. A metal rod would extend from the vehicle and touch the cable. Electricity from the cable then would travel back up the rod and power the car's motor. One big plus is that you'd never run out of gas. But a power failure would cause everybody to stop.

Most electric car designs today use batteries instead of rods and cables. Electric cars will be quiet and clean. They can help reduce air pollution in cities. Some electric cars already have been designed and tested. They can go as fast as gasoline-powered vehicles. Their chief drawback is that they can't go as far.

This electric car is being charged up while it is parked in a lot.

No one has yet been able to make a battery that can store as much energy as a tank of gasoline. Also, batteries large enough to run electric cars for very long take up most of the space in the car. So auto engineers are working on "hybrid" cars. These vehicles would combine small gasoline-powered engines with batteries.

One manufacturer has been testing a hybrid car that can go 100 miles an hour. It combines a small **turbine** engine and batteries. The problem, at present, is that the batteries are made of nickel and **cadmium**. Because these metals are very expensive, the batteries cost about $20,000. Engineers hope to bring the cost down in the future, enough to make an affordable model hybrid within 15 years. Another manufacturer is already selling a hybrid car.

automatic
(aw·tuh·**mat**·ik)—moving or working by itself

Stop and Ask

How does it connect to what I know? Decide whether I agree with what I am reading.

• • • • • • • • •

I agree that computers would solve lots of problems. I've seen my brother get distracted when he drives. With a computer, people wouldn't have to worry about making mistakes or falling asleep or getting lost.

turbine (**tur**·bin)— a machine that changes the motion of fluid into mechanical power

cadmium
(**kad**·mee·uhm)—a soft white metal used in some batteries

How does it connect to what I know? Decide whether I agree with what I am reading.

• • • • • • • • • •

I agree. I've seen other articles about the future of transportation. Many of them have mentioned that flying is the way we may get around in the future.

navigate (**nav·i·**gayt)— to steer

Other designs for future cars use lightweight plastic instead of metal. Some models actually shrink to make the cars easier to park. One manufacturer even has a design for a car that uses lasers and sensors to measure parking spaces. The car parks itself!

The Sky's the Limit

Sooner or later, there will be so much traffic on the roads that engineers may not be able to keep it moving. At that point, it might be time to rise above it all. Someday, people may fly around cities in their own private aircrafts! ? *Strategy Alert!*

Some people already have used this concept—sort of. For example, people sometimes fly around in "ultralight" aircraft, which are hang gliders with small engines. And a human-powered aircraft has flown across the English Channel.

A California aircraft designer, Dr. Paul Moller, has invented the M400 Skycar. The four-seat personal aircraft runs on regular gasoline and takes off and lands vertically like a helicopter. It uses a computer to **navigate**.

The Skycar can fly to heights of 30,000 feet—nearly six miles—and can go as fast as 390 miles an hour! That could cut daily commuting time to about 30 seconds. Unfortunately, you would need a pilot's license to fly the Skycar. And it costs about one million dollars. But Moller says that if his design ever goes into mass production, the price could drop to $60,000.

Inventor Paul Moller (inset) and some prototypes of the Skycar

Faster and Faster

If Skycar's 390 miles an hour still isn't fast enough, and 30,000 feet in the air still isn't high enough, then there's the HyperSoar. It's a super fast airplane, designed by the U.S. Department of Energy. It may be available as early as 2010. The HyperSoar will skip across the **atmosphere** like a stone across a pond.

The plane will zoom to 200,000 feet above Earth, nearly 40 miles up, almost into space. Then it will turn off its engines and coast back toward the edge of Earth's atmosphere. Here it will fire its engines, skip off the rim of the atmosphere, and climb into space again. Top speed? 6,700 miles an hour. The HyperSoar will be able to reach any spot on Earth in two hours. It will "skip" 25 times between New York and Tokyo. This would give new meaning to the phrase, "It's only a hop, skip, and a jump away."

Still not fast enough? Well, the space shuttle is getting old. The National Aeronautics and Space Administration (NASA) is bringing out the VentureStar, which will travel at 9,000 miles an hour. It will be able to take off from Earth under its own power. This is different from the shuttle, which requires booster rockets. (?) *Strategy Alert!*

The NASA logo

NASA says the VentureStar will be a space taxi, carrying satellites and people into space at about one tenth of the cost of a trip on the shuttle. NASA already is testing a **prototype,** called the *X-33*. The VentureStar could be ready for space missions in just a few years.

Stop and Ask

How does it connect to what I know? Decide whether I agree with what I am reading.

. . . .

It says that the VentureStar will be able to take off under its own power. I agree that should make it more useful. I can't imagine ordinary people using the space shuttle with its booster rockets. I've seen it lift off. It seems too dangerous!

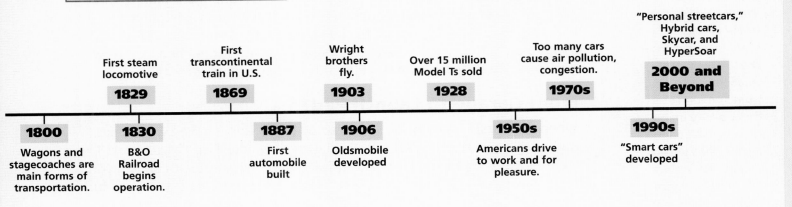

Transportation Time Line

1800	1829 / 1830	1869 / 1887	1903 / 1906	1928	1950s / 1970s	1990s / 2000 and Beyond

First steam locomotive — **1829**

First transcontinental train in U.S. — **1869**

Wright brothers fly. — **1903**

Over 15 million Model Ts sold — **1928**

Too many cars cause air pollution, congestion. — **1970s**

"Personal streetcars," Hybrid cars, Skycar, and HyperSoar — **2000 and Beyond**

1800 — Wagons and stagecoaches are main forms of transportation.

1830 — B&O Railroad begins operation.

1887 — First automobile built

1906 — Oldsmobile developed

1950s — Americans drive to work and for pleasure.

1990s — "Smart cars" developed

ABOVE: A "Maglev" train **INSET:** Electromagnets on the train and on the guideway repel each other, causing the train to lift.

mass transit
(mas **tran**·sit)—public transportation

levitation
(lev·i·**tay**·shuhn)—as if floating on air

Stop and Ask

How does it connect to what I know? Decide whether I agree with what I am reading.

● ● ● ● ● ● ● ● ● ● ●

I know there are already very fast trains in Japan. There is also a train that takes just three hours to go from London to Paris, partly under the English Channel. I agree that in the future, these kinds of trains will be even faster and more common.

Look, Ma, No Wheels!

Back on Earth, **mass transit** may take on an entirely new look. There will be no more noisy, dirty buses. Instead, people may float around cities on magnetic **levitation** trains. These sleek-looking trains will be suspended above their rails, or guideway.

Magnetic levitation works by fitting both the trains and the floor of the guideway with strong electromagnets and coils. When electricity is run around both sets of coils, the two sets of magnets repel each other, lifting the trains a few inches above the rails. Coils in the side of the guideway keep switching between negative and positive attraction. That pushes and pulls the train along the guideway.

These "Maglev" trains can move very fast. The Japanese plan to build a 310-mile system between Tokyo and Osaka. It will carry passengers between the two cities in a matter of minutes. Engineers are also thinking about a train that would travel in an underground tunnel between New York and Los Angeles (about 3,000 miles) in one hour. **②** *Strategy Alert!*

From Garage to Launch Pad?

When cars first came on the scene, some folks thought they were a passing fad. They shouted, "Get a horse!" when a Model T sputtered past. The technology of transportation has traveled light years since then. Are you ready to replace your garage with a launch pad? Don't do it just yet—but you might want to make plans!

> Congratulations! You finished reading. Now read the habit and strategy for **After I Read**. Then read my notes below.

After I Read

Which **HABIT** will I learn?

React to what I've read.

If I develop this habit, I will take time to think about what I've just read. Deciding what I think and what I feel helps me remember it better.

Which **STRATEGY** will I use to learn this habit?

Decide whether the author was objective or biased. Give reasons why I think so.

My Notes

- Strategy says to decide whether the author was objective or biased. That means to decide whether the author gave the facts on all sides of the issue (objective) or just told me one side of the story and gave his or her opinion (biased).

- The author discusses both good and bad things that happened because of cars.

- The author includes solid evidence, proving that the automobile has had some negative effects.

- I think the author presented both sides of the car issue.

Practice 3 of the 9 Habits

Now, it's time to practice the three habits and strategies you learned when you read "From the Horse to the Skycar." Start with **Before I Read**. Look at the box below. It should look familiar! Reread the habit you will practice. Reread the strategy you will use—then do it!

Before I Read

Which **HABIT** will I practice?
> **Think about what I know about the subject.**
> If I develop this habit, I will bring to mind what I already know about the subject. This gets me ready to connect what I read to what I know so I will understand it better.

Which **STRATEGY** will I use to practice this habit?
> Look at graphic aids, photos, and their captions to decide what I know about the subject.

 Use the **Before I Read Strategy Sheet** for "Medicine in the New Millennium" (page 48 in your *Strategy Practice Book*) to think about what you already know.

Medicine in the New Millennium

Dolly, the first genetically reproduced sheep, meets the press in Scotland, 1997.

The past century has seen many milestones in the field of medicine. Scientists discovered penicillin (the first antibiotic), unlocked the structure of DNA, and performed the world's first human heart transplant. The world's first "test-tube" baby was born. Most recently, a very special lamb named Dolly was born. She had been developed in a laboratory from a single cell of an adult sheep!

What does the future of medicine hold? Will cures for cancer, heart disease, spinal injuries, and other ailments be discovered? Will we order human organs like we do new cars? Will the "**bionic** person" become a reality? High-tech engineering methods have greatly benefited the field of medicine. So have developments in electronics. Technology has given doctors many new tools in the treatment of patients. So many possibilities lie ahead.

bionic (bie·on·ik)— consisting of mechanical devices

Reread the habit and strategy below. Look for the *Strategy Alerts!* as you continue to read.

While I Read

Which **HABIT** will I practice?

Stop and ask, "How does it connect to what I know?"

If I develop this habit, I will think about how what I'm reading fits with what I know. This helps me understand the new material and remember it better.

Which **STRATEGY** will I use to practice this habit?

Decide whether I agree with what I am reading.

Use the **While I Read Strategy Sheet** for "Medicine in the New Millennium" (page 49 in your *Strategy Practice Book*) as you read.

microlaser
(**mie**·kroh·**lay**·zuhr)—a very small device that sends out light waves in a very narrow and strong beam

Stop and Ask ❓

How does it connect to what I know? Decide whether I agree with what I am reading.

Scanning Methods

Today, doctors have several ways to look inside the human body without surgery. MRI (Magnetic Resonance Imaging) scans, CAT (Computerized Axial Tomography) scans, and ultrasound imaging use magnetic fields, x-rays, and sound waves to produce pictures of our internal organs. Some of these images are analyzed by computers. Then doctors use these images and data to diagnose a variety of health problems. As high-tech and useful as these methods are, they sound old-fashioned when compared to the scanning methods we might see in the future.

What lies ahead? Here are some millennial scanning tools some scientists predict will be found in the bathroom of the future. A **microlaser** embedded in your bathroom mirror will scan the back of your eye. It will measure the pressure in your eye, your blood pressure, and your oxygen level. Through a computer, it will notify your doctor of any problems it senses. Sensors in your toilet will analyze your waste for signs of blood or other problems. The information will be e-mailed to your doctor. A "smart" toothbrush will check for gum disease and cavities while it brushes your teeth. No doubt these breakthrough scanners will be popular because they will help your doctor treat you before you feel sick.

 Strategy Alert!

Implants

Implanted pacemakers help people with diseased hearts. They have been around for decades. Once implanted in the body, a pacemaker stimulates the heart to beat in a regular way. Future pacemakers will be tinier, easier to implant, and will not have batteries that need replacing.

Today's hearing aids merely increase the volume of the sounds that reach the ear. An electronic device called a *cochlear* [**kohk**·lee·uhr] *implant* is helping deaf people hear in a different way. A microchip in the implant turns sound waves into electronic signals. These signals are fed directly into the ear's nerves. Formerly deaf or severely hearing-impaired people can usually hear a wide range of sounds with the implant. Future implants will be even more sensitive.

Within a few years, a laser-powered microchip stapled to the **retina** will help blind people see. Here's how it will work. A small video camera in a pair of goggles will send images to the microchip. Electrodes on the chip then form an image that stimulates the retina, allowing the person to see.

implanted
(im·**plan**·tid)—inserted during surgery

retina (**ret**·n·uh)—part of the eye at the back of the eyeball

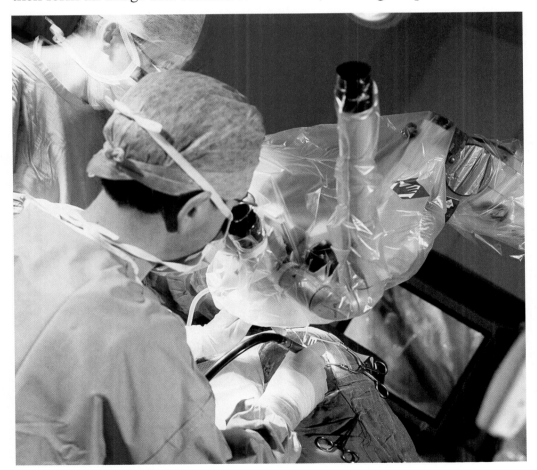

A surgeon uses a microscope with TV monitor to insert a cochlear implant into a deaf patient's ear.

Nanotechnology

Picture a swarm of germ-sized robots swimming through your blood vessels. Some measure your blood pressure as they move along. Some check your cholesterol, blood sugar, and hormone levels. Others look for problems such as blocked arteries and weak spots in artery walls. Still others hunt down cancer cells. All these things will be made possible by nanotechnology. Nanotechnology is a branch of engineering that deals with tiny machines. (*Nano* means "a billionth part.")

Researchers in this growing field hope to create miniature robots that can monitor people's bodies—from the inside! These machines will send the results to a main computer. The computer will analyze the data for signs of disease. If needed, the computer will send other nanomachines into your body. These will cure the specific problem. They will clean out a blocked artery or help your immune system fight off cancer cells.

Does this sound impossible? It may not be a reality yet, but scientists are working to make it so in the near future. Researchers have already developed tiny motors that are only 50 atoms long and have gears that are thinner than a human hair!  *Strategy Alert!*

Stop and Ask ?

How does it connect to what I know? Decide whether I agree with what I am reading.

Robotic Helpers

Surgeons often spend hours in an operating room performing painstaking procedures on critically ill patients. It is an exhausting job. Wouldn't it be helpful to have robots to take over? In fact, robot surgeons already help human doctors. They have been used to locate tumors and to guide a surgeon's scalpel. Robots have even drilled holes in bones during hip-replacement surgery. In Europe, robots have helped perform brain surgery! What can we expect of medical robots in the future?

Artificial intelligence (AI) researchers are creating computers that think and reason as humans do. AI robots can learn new tasks, correct their mistakes, and make complex decisions. Maybe AI robot surgeons will eventually operate on their own. ? *Strategy Alert!*

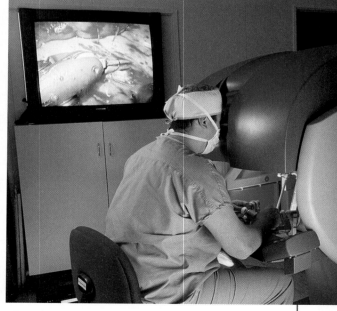

This surgeon uses the DaVinci robot to perform heart surgery.

Stop and Ask ?

How does it connect to what I know? Decide whether I agree with what I am reading.

Genetic Engineering and Gene Therapy

Are you tall or short, light or dark haired, musical or tone-deaf? It's all determined by your genes. Genes are the parts of cells that determine the traits an individual will have. They pass inherited characteristics—including some diseases—from parents to children. Genes help make us who we are, and faulty genes cause many health problems.

In 1990, two young girls became medical pioneers. Both were born with a faulty gene that kept their immune systems from fighting off infections. Both were in constant danger of dying from usually minor diseases. One girl never left her house for fear of infection. The other was constantly sick. Doctors created specially designed cells they hoped would strengthen the girls' immune systems. Each girl was injected with the gene-altered cells. Years later, both girls are alive and healthy. Their immune systems are strong. The experiment was a success.

In 1999, scientists from three countries announced that they had unlocked the **genetic** code of an entire human **chromosome**. This marked the first success in efforts to map the billions of genes that form a human being. Scientists hope that this knowledge will lead to advances in treating—or preventing—conditions caused by genetic defects. Scientists are now targeting diseases, such as hemophilia [hee·muh·**fil**·ee·uh] and diabetes, that gene therapy may cure. Hemophilia is a condition that results from a faulty gene that keeps the blood from clotting. Diabetes is a disease in which the body fails to produce enough insulin to regulate blood sugar levels. Gene replacement therapy may soon be able to treat these and other conditions.

genetic (juh·**net**·ik)—having to do with the passing on of characteristics from one person to another

chromosome (**kroh**·muh·sohm)—one of the tiny particles in cells that carry genes

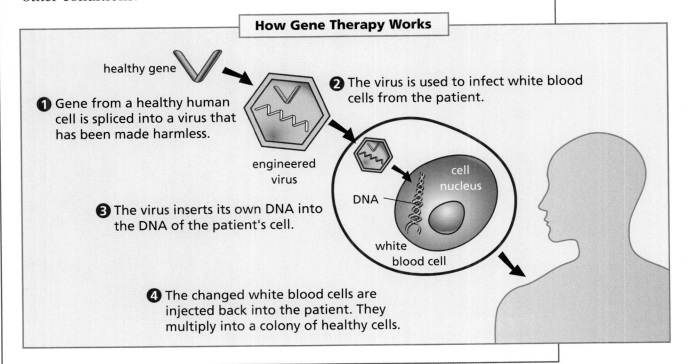

How Gene Therapy Works

healthy gene

❶ Gene from a healthy human cell is spliced into a virus that has been made harmless.

engineered virus

❷ The virus is used to infect white blood cells from the patient.

❸ The virus inserts its own DNA into the DNA of the patient's cell.

DNA

cell nucleus

white blood cell

❹ The changed white blood cells are injected back into the patient. They multiply into a colony of healthy cells.

Engineered Animals

Take an ordinary pig, add a tiny bit of mouse and a pinch of bacteria, and what do you get? A new kind of pig whose manure is less harmful to the environment than that of ordinary pigs!

Animals like that pig are created when "foreign" genes are placed into a single-celled **embryo**. Copies of the gene end up in each cell of the animal, giving it the new trait. The result is called a *transgenic animal*.

What does this mean for the future of medicine? Researchers have created sheep with some human genes. Milk produced by these sheep contains a substance that is used in medicine for humans. Scientists are trying to develop animals that produce different medicines in their milk. These living medicine factories should be on line in the near future. ⑦ *Strategy Alert!*

Organs Grown to Order

Not too long ago, the idea of exchanging diseased or injured body parts with healthy, whole ones was the stuff of science fiction. Yet surgeons have been transplanting organs from one human into another for decades. Kidney, liver, **cornea,** lung, and heart transplants are commonplace. More than 19,000 organ transplants are performed every year in the United States alone. Kidney and liver transplants can come from living donors. However, most transplant organs come from cadaver [kuh·**dav**·uhr] donors (that is, dead bodies). The need for healthy organs to transplant is far greater than the number of organs available. This is just one of the problems related to organ transplants.

These five cloned sheep are genetically identical.

---

embryo (**em**·bree·oh)— an animal in the first stages of development

Stop and Ask ❓

How does it connect to what I know? Decide whether I agree with what I am reading.

cornea (**kor**·nee·uh)— the clear, outer layer of the eyeball

Rejection of the donor organ is the greatest problem in transplants. The body tends to treat the new, transplanted organ as an invader. It attacks the organ and may kill it. As a result, transplant patients must take anti-rejection drugs throughout their lives. Researchers have been working on solving these problems by trying to grow organs "to order."

The most promising research is with stem cells. Most cells in our bodies—heart cells, bone cells, nerve cells, and so on—form just one type of tissue. Stem cells can turn into many kinds of tissue. Scientists are working at turning stem cells into other types of cells. Among other ailments, these cells could cure heart disease, spinal cord injuries, and some types of blindness. It may be just a matter of time until scientists achieve this goal. ⓐ *Strategy Alert!*

Stop and Ask ❓

How does it connect to what I know? Decide whether I agree with what I am reading.

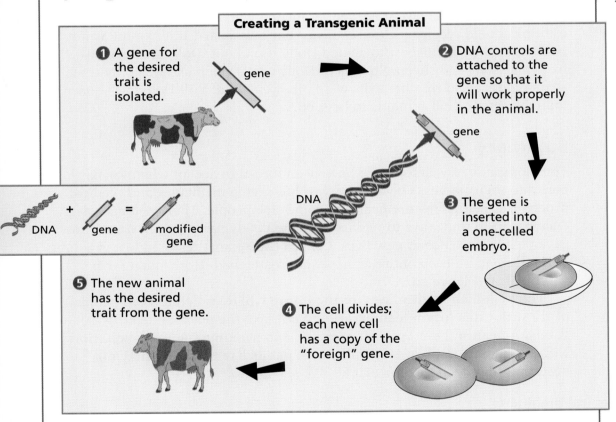

Creating a Transgenic Animal

❶ A gene for the desired trait is isolated.

❷ DNA controls are attached to the gene so that it will work properly in the animal.

❸ The gene is inserted into a one-celled embryo.

❹ The cell divides; each new cell has a copy of the "foreign" gene.

❺ The new animal has the desired trait from the gene.

DNA + gene = modified gene

Imagine being able to grow new fingers and toes like you grow new hair. Many animals are able to do this. Crabs, for example, can regrow **severed** legs. Starfish can regrow missing arms. Scientists have already grown human skin from patients' own cells and transplanted the skin successfully. In 2000, Japanese researchers announced that they had grown frog eyes and ears in a lab. Another researcher reported that he had grown frog kidneys. The results of such research may someday produce more than enough donor organs and end the problem of organ rejection.

severed (**sev**·uhrd)— having been cut or broken off

Cloning

Cloning is a process in which a whole new animal is created from a single cell taken from another animal. The clone is an exact twin of the other animal. Cloning began with a lamb named Dolly.

What are the benefits of cloning? Dairy farmers could clone their champion cows, producing more milk from smaller herds. Breeders of other animals could do the same. Endangered animals could be cloned to prevent extinction of the species. The frozen body of a woolly mammoth—a species extinct for 10,000 years—was found in Siberia. Some researchers think that new mammoths might be able to be cloned from its cells.

What possibilities does cloning have for humans? Cells from a person's organs could be collected and stored. New organs could be cloned and grown whenever they were needed. Someone who needed a new heart, for example, could receive a clone of his or her own heart! But cloning is not perfect, as the scientists who cloned Dolly found out. Dolly was cloned from a six-year-old sheep. Studies of Dolly's cells when she was only three years old revealed that her cells were nine years old! Will Dolly die sooner than expected? That remains to be seen.

Summary

For thousands of years, people have been forced to accept whatever happened to their bodies. The discovery of life-saving medicines and medical procedures helped restore health to some sick people. Then medical science began to find ways to replace damaged body parts. Organ transplants gave people a chance at new lives. Cornea transplants restored lost vision. Severed fingers—even entire arms—were reattached. How much farther will medical science go?

The high-tech medical care of the future will do much to keep people healthy. But this future technology will not take the place of healthy habits. A healthful diet, regular exercise, and avoiding high-risk behaviors will still be our best bet. Hopefully, with habits like those, we may not need that high-tech medicine at all! ⑦ *Strategy Alert!*

Stop and Ask ⑦

How does it connect to what I know? Decide whether I agree with what I am reading.

Twentieth Century Medical Highlights

1928	1953	1967	1972	1978	1990	1993	1997	1999
Discovery of penicillin	DNA's double-helix structure revealed	World's first human heart transplant	CAT scan invented	Birth of Louise Brown, the world's first test-tube baby	Gene therapy first performed	Gene that causes Huntington's disease located	Birth of Dolly, the first animal cloned from an adult cell; scientists clone sheep that produce medicine	Genetic code of chromosome 22 unlocked

Now that you've finished reading, review the **After I Read** habit below. Think about what you read in "Medicine in the New Millennium" as you practice the strategy.

After I Read

Which **HABIT** will I practice?
React to what I've read.
If I develop this habit, I will take time to think about what I've just read. Deciding what I think and what I feel helps me remember it better.

Which **STRATEGY** will I use to practice this habit?
Decide whether the author was objective or biased. Give reasons why I think so.

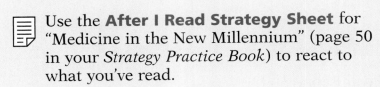 Use the **After I Read Strategy Sheet** for "Medicine in the New Millennium" (page 50 in your *Strategy Practice Book*) to react to what you've read.

> Now read "Space Colonies—Our Future Home?" and apply these three habits and strategies.

Before I Read

Which **HABIT** will I apply?
Think about what I know about the subject.

Which **STRATEGY** will I use to apply this habit?
Look at graphic aids, photos, and their captions to decide what I know about the subject.

While I Read

Which **HABIT** will I apply?
Stop and ask, "How does it connect to what I know?"

Which **STRATEGY** will I use to apply this habit?
Decide whether I agree with what I am reading.

After I Read

Which **HABIT** will I apply?
React to what I've read.

Which **STRATEGY** will I use to apply this habit?
Decide whether the author was objective or biased.
Give reasons why I think so.

Use the **Self-Assessment Sheet** for "Space Colonies" (pages 51–52 in your *Strategy Practice Book*) as you read to see how well you can apply the habits and strategies.

Space Colonies

Our Future Home?

Humans have a long history of exploration. People from Asia reached the Americas 10,000 years ago—when the only way to get there was to walk! Ancient sailors from Asia settled the islands of the Pacific Ocean beginning 5,000 years ago. Europeans first came to the New World 1,000 years ago. And the first modern explorers, beginning with Christopher Columbus, landed in the New World about 500 years ago.

Now, almost every livable piece of land on Earth has been settled by human beings. Every inch of the planet's surface has been photographed and studied by satellites. It's this need to explore that has caused us to turn our eyes to the possibility of life in other worlds. But where?

Human beings have walked on the moon, landed television cameras on Mars, and sent satellites toward the stars. Could outer space be the next place we inhabit? If so, when?

Columbus's fleet approaching land

Astronaut Edwin E. "Buzz" Aldrin walking on the moon

Still a Small Step

On July 16, 1969, three American astronauts rode the *Apollo 11* spacecraft to the moon. Four days later, two of them landed on the moon in an area called the Sea of Tranquility [tran·**kwil**·i·tee]. As billions of people on Earth listened to their radios, astronaut "Buzz" Aldrin described the **descent:** "Seventy-five feet. Things looking good. Lights on. Kicking up some dust. Thirty feet. Contact light! Okay. Engine stop."

Next, mission commander Neil Armstrong radioed his message to the control center in Houston, Texas: "Houston, Tranquility Base here. The *Eagle* has landed."

At the time, nearly every television in America was tuned in to the coverage of the *Apollo* mission. People all over the world watched Armstrong and Aldrin become the first humans to set foot on another world. Armstrong's words, "This is one small step for a man, one giant leap for mankind," have become one of the most famous quotations in history.

About 21 hours after Armstrong and Aldrin landed, earthbound TV watchers held their breath. A small camera relayed pictures back to Earth showing the top half of the *Eagle* landing craft as it blasted off from the moon's surface. The two men rejoined Michael Collins, the third astronaut, who had been waiting inside *Columbia*, the **orbiting** command ship.

descent (di·**sent**)—the act of lowering down

orbiting (**or**·bit·ing)—revolving around

Over the next three years, five more *Apollo* spacecraft landed on the moon. This got people thinking about the idea of building human colonies in space. But in the nearly 20 years since the last moon mission, not much progress has been made. So far, only half of Armstrong's quote has been true—it's only been "one small step."

The Next Few Steps

Science writer Isaac Asimov once said that if we want to settle other planets, we must first build colonies on the moon. He described how the moon's soil can be used to make the materials we would need to build settlements and structures in space. "Later," he said, "we can build cities underground on the moon, filling them with air and bringing in water from Earth." Asimov may only have been half-right. New studies of the moon have suggested that it may contain its own water. The water may be found frozen near the moon's south pole.

So far, however, we haven't taken any steps toward constructing moon colonies. Instead, we have been building space stations—**artificial** satellites that orbit Earth. Some astronauts have already lived in space for long periods. In the 1970s, three astronauts lived aboard America's huge *Skylab 4*. They stayed there for nearly three months! Russian crews have occupied the *Mir* space station **continuously** since 1986.

Now, America and several other nations are building a huge new space station. It will be about as long as a football field (including the end zones). On Earth, it would weigh about one million pounds—as heavy as 50 large trucks! The space station will be partially assembled on Earth. The assembled sections will be carried into orbit by America's space shuttles. When the space station is completed, it will orbit Earth from 220 miles away.

artificial
(ahr·tuh·**fish**·uhl)—made by humans

continuously
(kuhn·**tin**·yoo·uhs·lee)—without stopping

Russian Cosmonaut Valeri G. Korzun inside the *Mir* space station

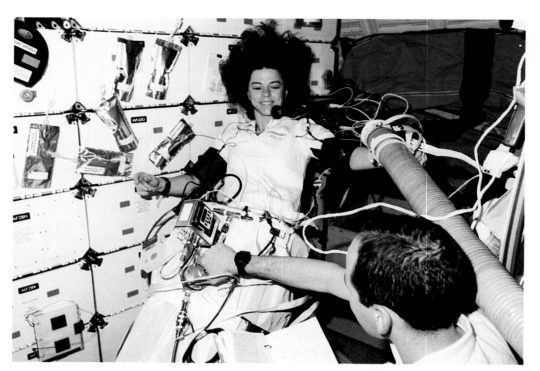

**Mission specialists experience weightlessness aboard the command ship,
Columbia.**

Beginning around 2005, the space station will host crews of six or
seven men and women at a time. These people will be mostly scientists.
Their job will be to study the effects of living and working in space for
long periods of time. They will remain on the station for a few months.
Then they will be relieved by new crew members, arriving on space
shuttle flights.

One of the most important things the scientists will study aboard the
space station is how humans cope with the lack of gravity. Gravity is the
force that keeps your feet on the ground, your pencil and paper on your
desk, and your breakfast cereal in your bowl! It also helps to keep your
bones and muscles strong.

Gravity on the space station will be about one millionth the strength
it is on Earth. So astronauts will have to walk lightly to avoid hitting their
heads on the ceiling! They will have to drink their soup from squeeze
bottles. Special exercise equipment will help them avoid losing bone and
muscle tissue.

The Best Way to Colonize?

Not everyone believes moon bases are the way to go. Some people believe
that the best way to colonize outer space is with large space stations. **Physics**
professor Gerard K. O'Neill is one of these people. He foresees a large fleet of
stations orbiting Earth. These structures would rotate to create artificial
gravity. And they would have large, glass-enclosed chambers to capture sunlight for growing food. O'Neill believes that someday space stations could
support 10 million people. That's more people than live in New York City!

physics (**fiz**·iks)—the
science dealing with
energy and matter

Others have argued that we might learn about space more quickly and cheaply from unpiloted space flights. Piloted flights, critics say, cost ten times as much as unpiloted flights. Such unpiloted flights have included the *Voyager* space probes, the *Hubble Space Telescope*, and the *Mars* lander.

After the Space Station

Nevertheless, colonies on the moon still may be our best bet for establishing a foothold in space. The moon offers several advantages as a site for a colony. For example, even though the moon is farther from Earth than orbiting space stations, it is still only a one- to two-day trip from Earth by rocket. Voice and video signals take only about three seconds—round trip! Also, the moon has minerals that can be used to build colonies and that are valuable on Earth. Its soil contains oxygen, crucial for breathing and a main ingredient in rocket fuel.

If the international space station is successful, space engineers may build a base on the moon. Some people even believe we need such a base as an "insurance policy." As Isaac Asimov wrote, "Humanity would have a second world. If Earth should be struck by an unexpected **catastrophe** . . . then a second world will exist on which humanity will survive."

There are several ways that colonies could spring up on the cold, gray, forbidding **lunar** surface. Ben Bova, another science writer, offers one possible plan. He imagines a dome nearly 2,000 feet wide and 250 feet high! This structure would be pumped full of air and covered by six feet of lunar soil. Inside this dome, colonists could build a village housing about 2,000 people. Bova believes the colony could pay for itself by mining valuable lunar minerals and shipping them back to Earth. The moon village could have trees, sidewalks, an orchestra, and many other things that make life enjoyable on Earth. Of course, life in the dome would have to be spent underground. Therefore it would lack some other Earth-like comforts, such as sunsets and seasonal changes.

catastrophe (kuh•**tas**•truh•fee)— disaster

lunar (**loo**•nuhr)—of the moon

One artist's impression of a base on the moon

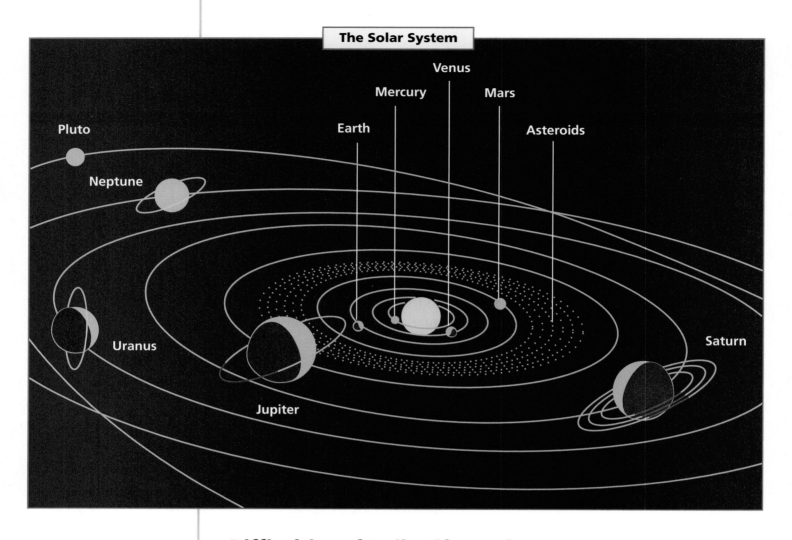

The Solar System

Difficulties of Daily Life on the Moon

A lunar colony would have to produce its own food. It would cost too much to deliver food by rockets. To farm successfully, the colony would need animals, plants, insects, and useful bacteria. Choosing these items would be a difficult and delicate job. Scientists would have to screen out anything that might harm the colony's health.

Lunar gravity is only one sixth that of Earth's gravity. That means a 150-pound person would weigh only 25 pounds on the moon! It would not be practical to build a colony that rotates to create artificial gravity. So the colonists would have to exercise often to keep their muscles toned.

The moon's lower gravity would create some unusual effects, however. For example, just about anybody could slam dunk a basketball! That would mean basketball hoops would have to be much higher than the standard 10 feet. Baseball fields would have to be much bigger because with less gravity, a talented professional ballplayer could hit the ball a mile!

On a practical level, rocket launches from the moon's surface would require much less fuel than launches from Earth. That makes the moon extremely valuable for something else in the future—sending rockets to the other planets. One of the first planets to be explored might be Mars.

Mars: The Red Planet

Ever since the Italian astronomer Galileo [gal·uh·**lay**·oh] studied Mars hundreds of years ago with his early telescope, this planet has fascinated people. Mars is the planet most like Earth—although its gravity is only two fifths as strong. The "Red Planet," as it is called because of its color in the night sky, has always appeared friendly and, well, livable.

In fact, in 1894, English **astronomer** Percival Lowell was peering through his telescope when he thought he saw straight lines crossing the planet's surface. These lines, Lowell concluded, were canals. They were built by Martians, he said, to bring water from the planet's ice caps to support their civilization.

It turned out there were no canals. When two American *Viking* space probes landed on Mars in 1976, they found the surface anything but **hospitable**. Temperatures on Mars are -220° Fahrenheit at the poles—or twice as cold as on Earth. Even at the Martian equator, the temperature only reaches about 68° F.

astronomer
(uh·**stron**·uh·muhr)—
a scientist who studies
the universe

hospitable
(**hos**·pi·tuh·buhl)—
favorable to growth and
development

**The surface
of Mars**

Comparing the Earth, Moon, and Mars			
	Earth	**Moon**	**Mars**
Diameter	7,921 miles	2,340 miles	4,421 miles
Surface temperature	−70C to +55C	−155C to +105C	−120C to +25C
Gravity (Earth = 1)	1	0.16	0.38
Water	Yes	No	Maybe
Planet surface	Mostly warm and wet	Dry and cold	Dry and cold
Atmosphere	98% oxygen and nitrogen	None	95% carbon dioxide
Tourist attractions	Variety of life, blue skies, oceans	Great view of Earth and space	Olympus Mons, 80,000+ feet high; Valles Marineris Canyon, about 2,500 miles long

Other Martian Drawbacks

Temperature isn't the only weather problem on Mars. Huge dust storms, driven by winds blowing hundreds of miles an hour, kick up and last for months at a time. The atmosphere is too thin to breathe and doesn't hold heat very well. The thin air fails to protect the surface from deadly solar **radiation**. Any life forms from Earth would die quickly on Mars.

The distance between Mars and Earth is yet another problem. A one-way trip to Mars would take six to nine months. Depending on where Earth and Mars are in their orbits around the sun, it would take people on Mars up to 20 minutes to receive a radio message from Earth. Plants and animals taken to Mars for food and farming would have to be tended very carefully. If they needed to be replaced, it would take a long time to send new animals and plants from Earth.

radiation
(ray·dee·**ay**·shuhn)—
energy that is sent out in waves

Channels on Mars

Martian Fossils?

So far, no spacecraft from Earth has found any life on Mars. But that doesn't mean life has never appeared on the Red Planet. For one thing, the Martian atmosphere is made up of some of the same elements as Earth's—carbon, oxygen, and nitrogen. Even though the concentrations are low, those three elements are necessary for life.

Something else favors the possibility that Mars once may have had life. Many scientists believe that when the planet was younger, it was warmer and wetter than it is now. It may even have had water in liquid form—instead of the ice that now covers the planet's poles. Anywhere there is water, there is a chance for life.

Whether the Martian water is ice or liquid, the more of it there is, the better it will be for possible future settlers. The presence of water helps in three ways: (1) there would be no need to transport it from Earth, (2) it will sustain people, animals, and plants, and (3) it can be broken down into its two parts—hydrogen and oxygen—to power rockets.

Chances are, if there ever was life on Mars, it probably was in the form of bacteria. It either died out long ago, or it clings to life somewhere in the Martian soil. Future missions to Mars may solve this mystery.

Sights of the Red Planet—and Beyond

Mars has some spectacular attractions. For example, the planet's highest mountain, Olympus Mons, towers more than 80,000 feet over the surface. Mt. Everest, the highest mountain here on Earth, seems tiny by comparison at about 29,000 feet. Then there is the canyon Valles Marineris. It is about 2,500 miles long. That's more than 10 times longer than Earth's Grand Canyon!

Just beyond Mars, there is another **potential habitat** that is not a planet at all. It is called the *asteroid belt*. Asteroids are small pieces of planets that contain many minerals valuable on Earth. Since they are relatively small, they could be hollowed out and have cities built inside. Since asteroids rotate, there would be artificial gravity inside.

Beyond Mars, there are four giant planets—Jupiter, Saturn, Uranus, and Neptune. All have environments too harsh to support humans. We may be able to colonize their smaller moons, however. We might even be able to do the same on tiny Pluto. From there, our sun would look like a faint star. Perhaps someday people will be able to use Pluto as a base from which to reach the stars.

Right now, no one knows exactly how we will colonize space. But progress is made every day. And it all began with those first small steps taken on the moon.

Mars Pathfinder **took this mosaic image of the surface of Mars.**

potential habitat (puh·**ten**·shuhl **hab**·i·tat)—possible environment

Put Your Habits to Work in

Literature | **Social Studies** | **Science** | **Math**

Before I Read Habit:
Think about what I know about the subject.

Remember to use graphic aids, photos, and captions in the text before you read a chapter in your science textbook. Look for charts, graphs, and tables. Decide what you know about the things the graphic aids and pictures show.

While I Read Habit:
Stop and ask, "How does it connect to what I know?"

As you read a chapter in your science textbook, stop and ask yourself whether you agree with what you're reading. Does it agree with what you know? Do you need to check further?

I agree the moon should be explored.

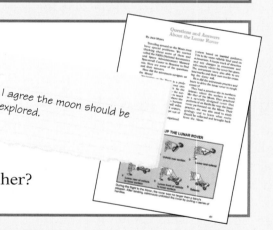

After I Read Habit:
React to what I've read.

You're not finished reading until you react to what you've read. You can do that by deciding whether the author was objective or biased. Then give reasons that tell why you think so.

This article gives only the facts . . .

You may wish to use the **Put Your Habits to Work Sheet** (page 53 in your *Strategy Practice Book*) to practice these habits in your other reading.

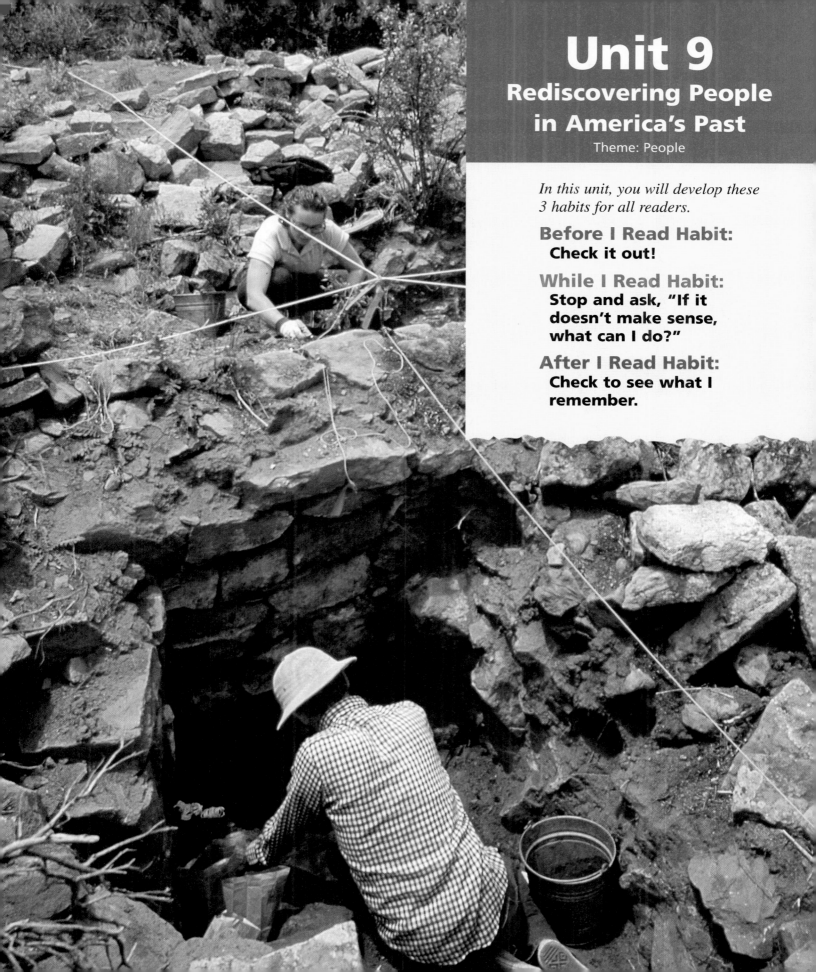

Unit 9
Rediscovering People in America's Past
Theme: People

In this unit, you will develop these 3 habits for all readers.

Before I Read Habit:
Check it out!

While I Read Habit:
Stop and ask, "If it doesn't make sense, what can I do?"

After I Read Habit:
Check to see what I remember.

Learn 3 of the 9 Habits

In this unit, you will learn three habits—one for before you read, one for while you are reading, and one for after you finish reading. Start with **Before I Read**. Read the habit and strategy. Then read my notes below.

Before I Read

Which **HABIT** will I learn?
Check it out!
If I develop this habit, I can find out something about what I am going to read so that I know what to expect.

Which **STRATEGY** will I use to learn this habit?
Decide which parts will best help me read for the reading purpose I have in mind.

My Notes

- Strategy says to decide which parts will help me read for my reading purpose.

- I guess I need to decide what my purpose is first. Am I reading just for fun? To find out some fact? To learn how to do something? Or just to learn about what I'm reading?

- I think I'm reading to learn more about mound builders. I think the sections titled "The Rise of Cahokia" and "Pyramids on the Mississippi" will be pretty helpful.

Mystery
of the
Mound Builders

In St. Louis, Missouri, shining glass and steel towers stretch above the Mississippi River. Here, you can see people using computers, fax machines, and cell phones. On the streets below, horns blare and brakes screech. Jet planes zoom overhead.

Eight miles to the east, the ruins of ancient life can be seen. About 60 earthen mounds rise above an otherwise flat landscape. Carved shell beads, pot **shards,** arrowheads, and human bones lie hidden in the earth. These are the remains of a great culture called Cahokia [kuh·**hoh**·kee·uh]. Some people have called Cahokia one of the great treasures of human history. Much has been learned about Cahokia, yet much remains unknown. What are these mounds? Who left them behind?

shards (shahrdz)— broken pieces; fragments

Now read the habit and strategy for **While I Read**. When you see , read my notes in the margin.

While I Read

Which HABIT will I learn?
Stop and ask, "If it doesn't make sense, what can I do?"
If I develop this habit, I will stop and figure out what to do so what I'm reading makes sense. Then I can keep reading and not be lost.

Which STRATEGY will I use to learn this habit?
Use word parts to help me understand words.

Stop and Ask

If it doesn't make sense, what can I do? Use word parts to help me understand words like *prehistoric*.

What does *prehistoric* mean? I know the prefix *pre-* means "before." *Historic* looks and sounds a lot like *history*. So *prehistoric* must have something to do with a time before history. It must mean "a long time ago."

artifacts (ahr·tuh·fakts)— things made by humans

Uncovering the Past

Explorers in the Mississippi Valley who saw these mounds in the 1600s wondered about them. Some were shaped like cones, while others were flat-topped pyramids. Still others looked like snakes and other animals. The Illini—local Native Americans—said that they did not know who had built the mounds. No stories had ever been told about them or their builders. They did say, however, that singing was sometimes heard at the mound sites just before dawn. It seemed obvious that humans, not nature, had built the mounds. But their purpose was still unknown.

Archaeologists—scientists who study past people and cultures—love mysteries. They especially love solving them. In the late 1800s, Cyrus Thomas, head of the Smithsonian Institution's Division of Mound Exploration, began studying the prehistoric mounds. Based on his research, Thomas deduced one important piece of information. He figured out that the mounds had once supported important buildings. For this reason, he gave these ancient builders the name "Temple Mound Builders." Thomas's deduction proved true. Temples had, in fact, stood atop many of the mounds. *Strategy Alert!*

The digging out of the mounds began in earnest in the early 1900s. When scientists began to dig, amazing treasures emerged from the earth. The **artifacts** astounded the scholars who discovered them. They found cups made of **conch** shells. They dug up carved wooden masks, human figures, and countless shell beads and copper ornaments. It was clear that these artifacts were created by people. But who had made these marvelous things? Where had these people come from? More important, why did they disappear?

An overview of the hills of Cahokia today

The Rise of Cahokia

People have been living in North America for tens of thousands of years. The earliest people gathered wild plants and hunted animals for food. At that time, people did not stay in one place long enough to grow crops. So, farming was not common. Prehistoric North Americans wandered from place to place in search of food. When the supply of wild plants and animals became scarce in one place, the people moved on.

This way of life changed around A.D. 900. Around this time, a hardy type of corn was introduced from Mexico. At about the same time, a period of global warming took place. The strong, healthy corn and a longer, warmer growing season combined to produce a plentiful crop. Instead of roaming from place to place in search of food, people formed farming settlements. Over hundreds of years, villages sprang up and the population grew. *Strategy Alert!*

Stop and Ask

If it doesn't make sense, what can I do? Use word parts to help me understand words like *plentiful*.

I know the suffix *-ful* means "full of." *Plenti* looks and sounds like *plenty*, which means "more than enough." So in this sentence, a *plentiful crop* must mean they had more than enough food.

Cahokia, around A.D. 1100

Stop and Ask

If it doesn't make sense, what can I do? Use word parts to help me understand words like *earthen*.

. . . .

I see the word *earth* and know it can mean "land or soil." I know the suffix *-en* can mean "made of," as in *wooden*. In this sentence, *earthen* must mean the mounds were "made of soil."

A new culture arose along the valleys of the Mississippi and Ohio rivers. Archaeologists named this the *Mississippian culture*. The people of the Mississippian culture had distinct customs, ideas, inventions, and tools. They built large towns with huge mounds made of dirt. On these mounds they built temples and other buildings. Cahokia was the largest of these ancient cities.

Cahokia grew into the largest city north of Mexico. It covered 4,000 acres and included more than 100 mounds. At its peak, around A.D. 1100, Cahokia was home to more than 20,000 people.

Pyramids on the Mississippi

Cahokia's most amazing feature was its earthen mounds. Many were huge, square-bottomed, flat-topped pyramids. Some served as bases for public buildings, homes of leaders, and temples. Others were graves or monuments to dead leaders. About 60 of these mounds still survive.
⑦ *Strategy Alert!*

At the vast plaza in Cahokia's center stood Monks Mound, which got its name in the 1700s from French **Trappist monks** who settled in the area. It is the largest earthwork in the Americas. This expansive pyramid covers more than 14 acres. It measures 700 feet by 1,080 feet at its base—roughly the size of 3 1/2 football fields—and rises in four **terraces** to a height of 100 feet! At one time, the mound was topped by a wooden building that was 105 feet long, 48 feet wide, and 50 feet high. This was probably the home of Cahokia's ruler. To build Monks Mound required more than 14 million baskets of soil, all hauled by human workers. Scholars say that it must have taken more than 300 years to build this amazing structure.

The people of Cahokia may not always have known peace with their neighbors. It is known that the central city was defended by a stockade. This sturdy wooden fence was formed by posts that were 12–15 feet high. There were guard towers every 70 feet along this wall. The stockade may have protected all the people of Cahokia at times of danger. It was rebuilt three times before the city was abandoned. Each time, about 15,000 new logs were used.

The **thatched** homes of the common people were beyond the walls of the central city. These straw-roofed buildings stretched for miles along both sides of the river. Fields of corn and other crops spread throughout the surrounding flood plains.

Trappist monks (**trap**·ist mungkz)— members of a religious brotherhood

terraces (**ter**·is·es)— raised banks of earth that are flat on top and have sloping sides

thatched (thachd)— roofing made of straw, palm leaves, and other plant stalks

Monks Mound

If it doesn't make sense, what can I do? Use word parts to help me understand words like *astronomy*.

• • • • • • • • • •

I know the prefix *astro-* means "stars" or "outer space." Astronomy must have something to do with learning about the stars or outer space.

equinox (ee·kwuh·noks)— the two times each year (spring and fall) when the length of day and night are equal

Woodhenge: An Ancient Solar Calendar

One of the most incredible finds is that some of Cahokia's people were skilled in math and astronomy. They knew a great deal about the movement of the sun, moon, planets, stars, and other heavenly bodies. Archaeologists know this from a ring of large cedar posts outside the stockade. They figured out that, when viewed in a certain way, the posts show the exact spot where the sun rises at key times of the year. These posts were actually a giant solar calendar! Scholars playfully named the circle *Woodhenge,* after a similar structure in England named "Stonehenge." Stonehenge is a circle of huge stones that ancient people also used as a solar calendar. The solar calendars in Cahokia and Stonehenge were set up to show the day on which each of the four seasons began. Today, we know those days are around March 21 (spring), June 21 (summer), September 21 (autumn), and December 21 (winter).

? *Strategy Alert!*

According to the solar calendar in Cahokia, the sun seems to rise from Monks Mound exactly on the spring **equinox**. In this way, the Cahokians knew when the spring planting season had arrived. Building a solar calendar that could predict when to safely plant required careful planning and vast knowledge.

Woodhenge reconstruction

A model of a thatched hut used by the people of Cahokia

Life in Cahokia

By studying the artifacts excavated from mounds, scholars can tell a great deal about life in Cahokia. The rulers of Cahokia lived in wooden buildings atop the highest mounds. As in other early societies, the rulers probably held **supreme** power over the lives of their people. Power and position would have been passed by birthright. This means that the power and titles of the rulers passed from one generation to the next, most likely from fathers to sons. *Strategy Alert!*

Cahokia had a successful hardware industry. Workers made hoes with flint blades and axes with shaped stone heads. Crafts such as pottery making, cloth making, and shell and copper working were practiced widely. Crafts persons dyed cloth and created new types of pottery. They produced shell beads and copper ornaments. Perhaps these beads were used for money or jewelry.

Cahokia sat near a place where several rivers come together. This made it the center of a large trade network. From far and near, people traveled the rivers to trade shells, copper, furs, hides, and other goods. Quite likely, Cahokia's central plaza was a marketplace. On days that were not market days, there might have been a festival or a sporting event in the plaza. Religious ceremonies no doubt played an important role in the lives of the residents as well.

supreme (soo•preem)— greatest

Stop and Ask ?

If it doesn't make sense, what can I do? Use word parts to help me understand words like *excavated*.

. . . .

I know the prefix *ex-* means "out of." The middle of this word reminds me of *cave* or *cavity*. I also know the suffix *-ed* means the word is in the past tense. So this might mean "dug out of a hole." I can check the dictionary.

descended
(di•**send**•ed)—came from
a certain source

nobles (**noe**•buhlz)—
people of high rank

litter (**lit**•uhr)—a couch
attached to long poles
and used to carry a
person

moccasins
(**mok**•uh•sinz)—soft
leather slippers worn by
Native Americans

Stop and Ask ?

If it doesn't make
sense, what can I do?
Use word parts to
help me understand
words like *structure*.

· · · · · · · · · · ·

I think *structure* is
related to *construct*,
which means "to
build." I know the suffix
-*ure* signals a noun. So
structure must be
something you build.
That makes sense in
this sentence.

A Window Into the Past

Scholars can tell all this about Cahokia from the artifacts they found, but artifacts tell only part of the story. Scholars have also learned about the lives of the people of Cahokia from studying other Mississippian communities. The Natchez were a group of Native Americans who **descended** from the mound builders. They carried on many customs of the mound-building tradition. In the 1700s, a Dutch settler lived among the Natchez for eight years. This man, Antoine Le Page du Pratz, wrote down all he saw and learned from the Natchez.

Through du Pratz, we know that the ruler of the Natchez was called the "Great Sun." He was supposed to have been the sun's own brother. Assisting the Great Sun was his earthly brother, Tattooed Serpent. Beneath them were the chiefs of other villages. Under these chiefs came the **nobles**. Lowest of all were the commoners who did the work of the tribe. They grew the food and carried the soil to build the mounds.

The Great Sun lived on top of one of the tallest mounds. He wore a crown of white feathers. His feet never touched bare ground. When he walked, mats were spread before him. Most of the time, he was carried on a flower-decked **litter**. Archaeologists have found remains of such carrying vehicles in burial mounds. The Great Sun had total power over his people's lives and property.

When the Great Sun died, he was not buried alone. His wives, all of his servants, and others were killed to be with him in the next world. Excavation of one mound in Cahokia proves this was true. In this mound, a man about 45 years old lay on a carpet made of thousands of shell beads. Near him was a pit full of other bodies—4 men and 53 women—all between the ages of 15 and 25.

In 1725, du Pratz got to see an actual burial ceremony. The Natchez's war chief, Tattooed Serpent, died. His body was dressed in finely decorated clothes and painted in bright colors. He wore **moccasins** for his journey into the next world. In keeping with custom, his two wives, his sister, and many others were strangled and buried with him. After the ceremony, his house was burned to the ground. In earlier times, it would have been covered with soil to form a higher mound. Later, a new structure would have appeared on top.

 Strategy Alert!

This sketch, "Dance General," is from du Pratz's sketchbook of life among the Natchez.

But this time the Natchez could not carry out their custom. Illness brought from Europe had weakened the Natchez and reduced their numbers. In 1729, the remaining Natchez were killed in a war with France. With them, the last signs of Mississippian culture died, too. Did the Cahokians meet a similar fate? Did they also fall victims to war and disease?

The End of Cahokia

Experts know that around 1250, the population of Cahokia began to shrink. The great city became a smaller village. By 1500, it had been totally abandoned. Why? Many things may have led to the end of this culture. Around 1250, the climate became cooler and drier. This period has been called the "Little Ice Age." The cooler weather may have shortened the growing season. Whole forests had been cleared for firewood, buildings, and stockades. People had to travel farther to gather wood for fires and other purposes. Tree cutting also destroyed wildlife habitat. Food may have become scarce.

At the same time, problems may have developed in the cities. **Overpopulation** and lack of sanitary systems may have combined to cause the spread of disease. Cahokia had no systems for getting rid of garbage and human waste. Finally, European settlers brought with them diseases unknown in the Americas. These diseases spread quickly.

Whatever the causes, Cahokia was abandoned. This did not happen all at once. Archaeological evidence indicates a gradual loss of population over a period of 200 years. At last, Cahokia was no more. For centuries it lay hidden and forgotten, until the excavations began.

overpopulation (oh·vuhr·pop·yuh·**lay**·shuhn)—crowding caused by too many people

backhoes (bak·hohz)— large machines for digging

ensure (en·shoor)— to make certain

Saving Cahokia

Some of the earliest excavations of the mounds were carried out violently. Treasure hunters discovered the mounds and ripped them apart as they tunneled through the mounds. Some even blasted into them with dynamite. Archaeologists tried to stop this. More artifacts were being destroyed than were found.

Then, in the 1960s, Cahokia itself was threatened. Plans for a highway to go through the site would have destroyed it. Archaeologists made a desperate attempt to save this treasure. Racing against time, they excavated many mounds before they could be destroyed forever. Finally, they won the fight to save the mounds. The highway was rerouted. ❓ *Strategy Alert!*

Much has been learned about Cahokia. Much is still to be learned. Modern technology has replaced shovels, dynamite, and **backhoes.** A team of researchers is exploring the site with high-tech instruments. These tools can read what lies beneath the surface of the ground without disturbing it. They can show the locations of buried buildings without digging them up. Computers analyze the information. In this way, archaeologists can **ensure** that Cahokia will not disappear again. It will remain a window into our country's past—for us and for those who come after.

ABOVE: Sunrise over Cahokia INSET: Steep steps give visitors access to the top of the mounds.

Congratulations! You finished reading. Now read the habit and strategy for **After I Read**. Then read my notes below.

After I Read

Which **HABIT** will I learn?

Check to see what I remember.

If I develop this habit, I will check to see what I remember as soon as I finish reading. It helps me see if I really understood what I read and helps me remember it better, too.

Which **STRATEGY** will I use to learn this habit?

Use examples or explanations from the text to question myself about what I've read.

My Notes

- Strategy says to use examples or explanations to question myself.

- I remember reading an explanation of mounds in the article.

- Here are some questions I can ask myself: Who made the mounds? What were they used for?

- An example of an interesting find is the ring of posts called "Woodhenge." Here's a question I can ask myself: What was Woodhenge used for?

- If I answer these questions, I can see what I remember.

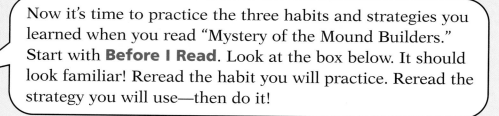

Now it's time to practice the three habits and strategies you learned when you read "Mystery of the Mound Builders." Start with **Before I Read**. Look at the box below. It should look familiar! Reread the habit you will practice. Reread the strategy you will use—then do it!

Before I Read

Which **HABIT** will I practice?
Check it out!
If I develop this habit, I can find out something about what I am going to read so that I know what to expect.

Which **STRATEGY** will I use to practice this habit?
Decide which parts will best help me read for the reading purpose I have in mind.

 Use the **Before I Read Strategy Sheet** for "In Search of Jamestown" (page 54 in your *Strategy Practice Book*) to check it out.

In Search of Jamestown

Archaeologist Bill Kelso excavating the Jamestown site

In December of 1606, one hundred men and four boys left England. They were seeking riches and a new life in a new land, America. That new life began in the fort they built at Jamestown, the first permanent English settlement in America. But the men disappeared and so did the fort—until an archaeologist brought the fort back to life.

For a long time, it was believed that the **remnants** of James Fort had been carried away by the James River. Many archaeologists had searched for the fort, but none had found the prize. As a college student in the 1960s, future archaeologist Bill Kelso had explored Jamestown Island and found dirt layers covered with artifacts from later colonists, the Civil War, and native peoples. Why couldn't the James Fort have survived the river, too? In April 1994, Kelso and his team got the chance to begin digging for James Fort in earnest.

"I was digging with a shovel and putting the dirt through a screen," Kelso said. "I brushed aside the dirt and there it was—part of a very old clay pipe."

Other archaeologists had searched for the fort. Could that pipe mean that this dig site was the actual location of the historic fort?

remnants (rem·nuhnts)— small parts that remained

Clay pipe found at the site

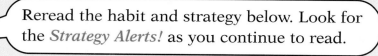

Reread the habit and strategy below. Look for the *Strategy Alerts!* as you continue to read.

While I Read

Which **HABIT** will I practice?

Stop and ask, "If it doesn't make sense, what can I do?"
If I develop this habit, I will stop and figure out what to do so what I'm reading makes sense. Then I can keep reading and not be lost.

Which **STRATEGY** will I use to practice this habit?
Use word parts to help me understand words.

 Use the **While I Read Strategy Sheet** for "In Search of Jamestown" (page 55 in your *Strategy Practice Book*) as you read.

Danger and Mystery

Nearly 400 years before Kelso's find, a group of men from England boarded a sailing ship and headed for America. They had been given a charter—or contract—from their king, James I. It allowed the men to set up a colony in the New World. Around the same time, the kings and queens of France, Holland, and Spain were also sending groups to America. Everyone had the same orders: search for gold and other riches, and find a shorter trade route to Asia.

In the early 1600s, crossing the Atlantic Ocean was difficult and perilous.* The journey could take months. Ships were often lost in storms at sea. They also sank after hitting **reefs** within sight of unknown shores. Fresh food lasted only a few days. After that, sailors and passengers ate poorly preserved meat or whatever fish they could catch. Many grew ill and died from disease. *Strategy Alert!*

Worse still, the dangers didn't end at sea. Back then, America was a nearly unknown land to Europeans. They didn't know about the poison ivy, copperhead snakes, and ticks that lurked in this new land.

reefs—strips of rock, sand, or coral that sit just below the surface of the water

If it doesn't make sense, what can I do? Use word parts to help me understand words like *perilous.*

Also, when settlers from Europe arrived, America was already inhabited by native people. These native Americans were prepared to fight to defend their land, which Europeans were trying to claim as their own. News of battles in which settlers had been killed had already reached England. It was for this reason that the settlers first built their fort.

Why would anyone take such a risky journey? Why would the men leave their families? Why would they travel to a strange land, from which they might not be able to return home for years?

The Chance to Become Rich

Many people left their homes in Europe for the chance to become rich. People who signed up to be colonists might succeed at farming or some kind of business in the New World—if they survived crossing the Atlantic.

The Englishmen landed on the eastern shore of what is now the state of Virginia. They intended to build a small settlement, or village. From it, they could begin to prepare the surrounding land for farming. They also could use the settlement as a base from which to explore the unknown land.

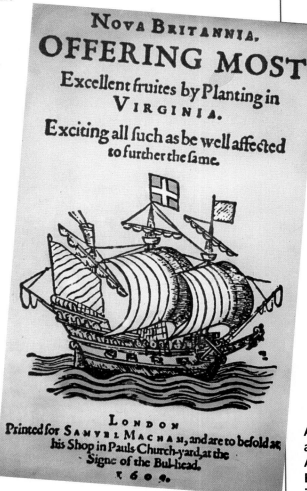

A poster advertising America to Englishmen in 1609

habitation (hab·i·**tay**·shuhn)— residence

sustained (suh·**staynd**)—supplied with food

Virginia seemed beautiful. Captain John Smith, one of the group's leaders, wrote that "heaven and earth never agreed better to frame a place for man's **habitation**...." In May 1607, the English colonists decided to begin building a settlement on an island in the middle of a river. They named that river the James. They named the island James as well. And they named their settlement Jamestown, all after their king.

The native people they met had lived in the same area for thousands of years. The rich land **sustained** many tribes of native people. There were plenty of animals to hunt, lots of fish, and many wild plants to gather for food. The Indians planted a crop called *maize*, which we now call *corn*. They also planted a type of tobacco, which they smoked in clay pipes.

But the English colonists were not hunters, fishermen, or farmers. About half their number were "gentlemen." The rest were artisans* and laborers. They also had little idea what it would be like to start a settlement in the wilderness. They only knew that if they were successful, they would become landowners in the New World. (?) *Strategy Alert!*

These men chose to build their Jamestown settlement on the island because the river was deep nearby. It allowed them to anchor their ships close to shore. But it was not the best place to build a settlement. Soon after they arrived in May, the summer heat and dampness arrived too. It rotted their food and clothing. Summer also brought millions of disease-carrying insects. And growing crops in the marshy soil proved to be difficult for these inexperienced farmers.

Stop and Ask (?)

If it doesn't make sense, what can I do? Use word parts to help me understand words like *artisans.*

Early settlers building the fort at Jamestown

The First Challenge

The 104 colonists would learn about all of those problems later. But their first challenge arose from the 10,000 native people who lived all around them.

Because of their earlier experiences with Spanish settlers, the Indians did not greet the English with open arms. They attacked the settlers almost immediately. Armor, swords, and **muskets** found around the area of the settlement seem to show that many of these "gentlemen" must have been experienced soldiers. They realized the need for a fort to protect themselves against the natives. Records show that in about a month, the men had built a simple wooden fort in the shape of a triangle. This fort would protect the buildings inside. They named it James Fort.

muskets (**mus**·kits)— long-barreled guns used before rifles were invented

Piecing the Past Together

Using archaeology to discover Jamestown's history is not easy. You can't simply walk around the site and pick up artifacts lying on the ground. Usually, artifacts aren't even in one piece. Small bits must be gathered from careful digging over a large area.

One of the biggest problems with the Jamestown site was that it had been used as farmland. Although the Jamestown settlers had little luck with farming, later inhabitants were more skilled. The archaeologists found that the land had been disturbed many times over the years. The dirt was plowed each time crops were planted. This made it more difficult to study the remains of Jamestown that were buried in the soil.

Mysterious Stains

Early in the dig, Kelso's team found dark stains in the soil. They knew that when wood rots, it often leaves a stain in the soil. The team **speculated** that the stains they saw had been left by the posts the colonists had sunk to hold the walls of their fort. But the archaeologists couldn't be sure. In order to prove their theory, they had to do two things. First they had to show that the locations of the stains matched the locations of the posts in old documents describing the fort. Second, they had to prove that the artifacts they found near the stains came from the same time that the Jamestown colonists landed—the early seventeenth century.

During the first year of this dig—1994—the archaeologists had found lots of items that were old enough to have been used by the colonists. They kept digging.

speculated (**spek·yuh·lay·tid**)— considered; made guesses

A fishhook found at the Jamestown site

An overview of the Jamestown Fort in Virginia as imagined by a modern artist

Bill Kelso at the site

trench—a ditch

Stop and Ask ?

If it doesn't make sense, what can I do? Use word parts to help me understand words like *dwelling*.

By 1996, they had found enough stains to plot them against old fort maps. Those maps showed that the structure had been a "palisade." It used heavy posts sunk deep in the ground. In between, narrow wood boards were sunk side by side into a narrow **trench**. Behind the boards, a dirt-filled shelf was built. From the outside, the fort's tall walls would be difficult to climb. But from the inside, the settlers could stand on the dirt shelf and rest their guns on top of the boards.

Kelso and his team carefully compared the stains in the soil against the post holes on the map. They matched! The two sides of the fort came together at exactly 46 1/2 degrees, the exact angle shown in the old documents. The lost fort had not washed away after all!

Over the years, archaeologists have uncovered more than 160,000 artifacts at Jamestown and other nearby sites. The fort, which had been thought to be gone forever, and its artifacts have shed new light on the lives of these settlers who came so far so long ago.

Evidence of Hard Times

Written reports also suggested that the fort had buildings for dwelling* and storage inside. What the team found led them to believe this was true. Pieces of glass bottles, cooking pots, and dishes left little doubt that people had lived inside the fort. Many copper beads and ornaments were also found at the Jamestown site. The Indians valued copper as much as the English valued gold. During those years, the Jamestown colonists seldom had enough food. As supplies began to run out, the settlers traded these beads and ornaments for maize and other foods. Archaeologists have even found evidence that the settlers began to make beads to trade.

Jamestown settlers trading with Indians inside the fort

The more new settlers arrived from England, the worse the situation grew. The winter of 1609–1610 was very hard. By 1610, of the more than 500 settlers who had arrived, only about 60 survived. Later settlers called that winter "the starving time." Then, between 1619 and 1621, another 3,560 people were sent from England to Jamestown. Of those, about 2,500 died within three years.

Not everyone died from natural causes. Archaeologists found a skeleton of a young man who had been shot with a musket ball. This man may have bled to death after he attempted to leave the settlement during the colony's first year.

Archaeologists have found the graves of many of those poor souls. J. Lawrence Angel, a bone expert from the Smithsonian Institution, examined some of the skeletons in the graves. "The most startling thing about the skeletons is their youth," Angel said. For example, of the human remains in 15 graves discovered at Jamestown, no one was older than about 32 at their time of death.

A skeleton found at the site

A Threat to the Indians

Indians posed a frequent threat to the Jamestown settlers. But the settlers posed a great danger to the Indians as well. The settlers brought diseases for which the Indians had no natural defenses. Diseases such as smallpox nearly wiped out the native population. By 1670, only about 4,000 native people populated the area. The rest had died or had been driven out.

Disease took its toll on the English, too. Over the life of the Jamestown colony, chances of survival were very slim. If 12 people arrived, only one of them was likely to survive. Diseases were caused by poor sanitation,* bad diet, or **malaria**-carrying mosquitoes. **Contagious** diseases spread quickly in the close living quarters. If disease did not kill the English, then chances were high that they would die from fire, starvation, or Indian attack. *⃝ Strategy Alert!*

In 1622, the local Indians attacked the Jamestown colony again. This time they killed 347 residents. By 1624, the remaining residents of Jamestown had moved to new colonies outside the fort.

malaria
(muh·**lair**·ee·uh)—
a disease

contagious
(kuhn·**tay**·juhs)—
spreading from one to another

Stop and Ask ❓

If it doesn't make sense, what can I do? Use word parts to help me understand words like *sanitation*.

A jug found at the site

imported (im·**por**·tid)—
carried or brought in

Stop and Ask

If it doesn't make
sense, what can I do?
Use word parts to
help me understand
words like *signet*.

Evidence of Some Better Times

Even though life in Jamestown was harsh, the colony enjoyed peaceful times, too. Again, archaeology has provided some of the evidence. Pieces of musical instruments have been found at the site. That tells us that the settlers must have taken some time off for singing and dancing. Gaming pieces and dice offer additional clues about leisure time. And two types of clay pipes were found. One type was **imported** from England and the other was made from local clay. The men must have had some time to smoke them.

Bits of jewelry and ceramics tell us even more about the settlers. For example, a signet* ring was found at Jamestown. Its owner must have been an important person, because his ring would have been used to stamp official documents. 🄫 *Strategy Alert!*

Broken pieces of ceramic pots tell us about Jamestown's trade. Some of the pots came from Holland and Italy. Some came from as far away as China. And some were made from local clay. The imported pots were most likely traded for tobacco, food, lumber, or coins when ships passed through the area.

James Fort Day

By the end of the summer of 1996, the evidence ruled out the chances that what Kelso and his team had found could be anything other than James Fort. September 12, 1996 was declared "James Fort Day" in Virginia. Governor George Allen announced that, despite earlier fears that it had been washed away, the old fort was still present in Virginia.

Each new artifact uncovered at the Jamestown site tells us a little more about the lives of the people who lived in that historic colony.

"This is the stuff of our history," Kelso says, "and I like to figure out what stories it has to tell."

Visitors to the Jamestown Fort learn about life in Jamestown during the 1600s from an actor portraying one of the colonists.

Now that you've finished reading, review the **After I Read** habit below. Think about what you read in "In Search of Jamestown" as you practice the strategy.

After I Read

Which **HABIT** will I practice?
Check to see what I remember.
If I develop this habit, I will check to see what I remember as soon as I finish reading. It helps me see if I really understood what I read and helps me remember it better, too.

Which **STRATEGY** will I use to practice this habit?
Use examples or explanations from the text to question myself about what I've read.

 Use the **After I Read Strategy Sheet** for "In Search of Jamestown" (page 56 in your *Strategy Practice Book*) to see what you remember.

Apply 3 of the 9 Habits

> Now read "Urban Archaeology" and apply these habits and strategies.

Before I Read

Which **HABIT** will I apply?
Check it out!

Which **STRATEGY** will I use to apply this habit?
Decide which parts will best help me read for the reading purpose I have in mind.

While I Read

Which **HABIT** will I apply?
Stop and ask, "If it doesn't make sense, what can I do?"

Which **STRATEGY** will I use to apply this habit?
Use word parts to help me understand words.

After I Read

Which **HABIT** will I apply?
Check to see what I remember.

Which **STRATEGY** will I use to apply this habit?
Use examples or explanations from the text to question myself about what I've read.

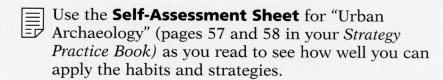
Use the **Self-Assessment Sheet** for "Urban Archaeology" (pages 57 and 58 in your *Strategy Practice Book)* as you read to see how well you can apply the habits and strategies.

Urban Archaeology
Peeling the Big Apple

Introduction

What do you think of when you think of archaeology? If you're like most people, you probably think "ancient," "thousands of years ago," "B.C."! The tombs of the pharaohs in Egypt, the lost cities of the Incas—they're what archaeology is about. That's true, of course. But archaeology isn't only about civilizations that existed thousands of years ago. Archaeology can also help us understand the more recent past.

In fact, since the 1990s, archaeologists have been excavating an area of the United States that was inhabited as recently as 50 years ago. They have been digging out a section of "The Big Apple," an affectionate nickname for New York City. This section was the site of a poor working-class neighborhood that, in the 1800s, was known as Five Points.

Learning From Objects

Archaeologists learn about the past by studying the objects that remain. They dig carefully to uncover artifacts, things that were made and used by people in the past. They study them to learn about the lives of people who owned them. With this information, they construct a picture of what life was like in an earlier time. Joan Geismar, past-president of the Professional Archaeologists of New York City, said it simply: "Archaeology deals with garbage."

But artifacts—the pottery and bottles and tools of a people—tell a lot about daily life. Historical documents provide only an official record of events. They don't necessarily shed light on what life was like for the ordinary people who lived through those events. Archaeological discoveries add another important **dimension** to really understanding a culture.

The Layout of Lower Manhattan

Today, New York City is made up of five areas, called *boroughs*. The boroughs are Manhattan, Brooklyn, The Bronx, Queens, and Staten Island. But until 1874, New York City consisted of only Manhattan, an island about 2 miles wide and 12 miles long. It is bordered by the East River, the Harlem River, the Hudson River, and New York Harbor. For almost 400 years, this island has been the site of settlement and **commerce**.

dimension (di·**men**·shuhn)—side; way of looking at

commerce (**kom**·uhrs)— the buying and selling of goods

A bird's-eye view of Manhattan and parts of Brooklyn

Wall Street and the New York Stock Exchange today

In New York City, change seems to be the only constant. Old buildings are demolished and new buildings crop up on the same sites. This cycle of development has gone on all over the city, but especially in lower Manhattan. The southern tip of the island, which **juts** out into New York Harbor, is the oldest part of the city. When you visit lower Manhattan, you can tell that it's old. The buildings are not what tell you the area is old—you have to look hard to find buildings that were built before the twentieth century. It's the layout of the streets that tells you that this part of the city is old. Farther uptown, away from the harbor, New York City is a neat grid of straight streets and avenues. But in lower Manhattan there is no particular pattern to the streets. They are not straight. They do not intersect at right angles. Many of them are only two or three blocks long. These streets were not planned. They developed from wagon trails, along the boundaries of farms, and around a pond.

juts—sticks out

A Lower Manhattan Neighborhood in the 1800s

In lower Manhattan today, you will find crowds of people in a big hurry. You will find the historic buildings of the New York Stock Exchange and the towering World Trade Center. You might find it hard to believe that

Broadway block in the 1880s

there once was a large freshwater pond here. Collect Pond was the largest body of fresh water in the city. Beside Collect Pond was a neighborhood known as Five Points. It was named for the "five points" formed by the intersection of Baxter, Park, and Worth Streets. By the late 1700s, many industries had grown up around Collect Pond. A row of **tanneries** stood along the eastern outlet of the pond. There were also slaughterhouses, breweries, potteries, and ropewalks—alleys where hemp fiber was laid and twisted into rope. These industries created a terrible smell and polluted the pond. Eventually, Collect Pond became so polluted that it presented a serious health **hazard** and had to be filled in. This neighborhood was not an appealing place to live.

tanneries (tan·uh·reez)— places where leather is made

hazard (haz·uhrd)— a possible source of danger

Overpopulation in Five Points

By the 1820s, the population of New York City was growing rapidly. As a result, there was a great housing shortage. The city began expanding northward. Landlords in Five Points divided their houses into rental units. Where one family once lived, now there were several families. Five Points was overcrowded by the 1840s. Most of the people who lived there were newly arrived immigrants. Between 1840 and 1860, nearly three million immigrants had come to the city from northwestern Europe. Of those, about 500,000 made their homes in the city. They lived in tenement buildings with no indoor plumbing and poor

Wood engraving showing tenements near Five Points

sanitary facilities. The living conditions gave Five Points the appearance of a terrible slum. Accounts from that period describe a run-down neighborhood that was poor, overcrowded, and troubled by violence.

The English novelist Charles Dickens visited Five Points in 1842. Dickens wrote many of his stories about characters living in poverty in England. This is how he described Five Points after his visit: "This is the place: these narrow ways **diverging** to the right and left, and reeking everywhere with dirt and filth..."

In the middle of the nineteenth century, Five Points was, by **contemporary** accounts, New York's best-known slum.

A Surprising Discovery

In 1991, the Federal government was preparing to build a new courthouse at Foley Square. The site had been part of the old Five Points neighborhood. When workers began to dig the foundation, they made some surprising discoveries, including the skeletal remains of nearly 400 people of African ancestry.

While the skeletons must have surprised the construction workers, archaeologist Dr. Rebecca Yamin readily explained them: "Free and enslaved Africans had been burying their dead on land southwest of the Collect Pond since the early 1700s. They had carried out religious rites there and used it as a gathering place when none other was available."

diverging (di·**vur**·jing)—going in different directions

contemporary (kuhn·**tem**·puh·rer·ee)—current; recent

The excavation of the African Burial Ground was the beginning of the archaeological exploration of Five Points. In all, 22 places were excavated. Most of these places had been old backyards and included **privies, cisterns,** and wells. Researchers found artifacts; the past people who had left them would have called them "trash." But trash can tell a lot about people's day-to-day lives. The artifacts found at Five Points give an impression of life that is different from the one provided by contemporary writers such as Dickens.

A Thriving Neighborhood

In the nineteenth century, Five Points was a mixed residential, commercial, and industrial area. Homes, shops, and factories were all located on the same streets. Along Chatham Street, for example, most of the buildings had shops on the ground floor and residential apartments above. The shops sold such things as shoes, children's clothing, furniture, and jewelry. Many of the shopkeepers would display their goods in front of their shops. Peddlers sold their wares from carts in the street. There were also restaurants, theaters, and beer gardens on Chatham Street. By day and by night, Chatham Street was busy.

Maps, **deeds,** and population records added to the archaeologists' information about Chatham Street and the area around Collect Pond. That's how they learned about Tobias Hoffman. Tobias and his wife, Margaret, ran a bakery in Five Points and lived in a house next door. The family's nearness to the stinky tanneries would give the impression that they were probably not well-off. Yet archaeologists uncovered pieces of fancy Chinese porcelain and English drinking glasses. Apparently, Mr. and Mrs. Hoffman had set a lovely table!

privies (priv·eez)— outhouses; toilets

cisterns (sis·tuhrnz)— containers for catching and holding rainwater

deeds—official papers, usually relating to owned land

This 1866 engraving shows the shared backyards on Manhattan's East Side.

By the early 1800s, the tanneries along the eastern outlet of Collect Pond had closed. The area became Pearl Street. Houses and shops replaced the tanneries. From 1865 to 1873, John Lysaight ran a saloon on the ground floor of the tenement at 474 Pearl Street. On the site of this saloon, archaeologists found glasses, bottles, and a **spittoon**. This was the usual trash for a saloon. But they also found ink bottles. The ink bottles suggest that this saloon, like many others of its time, was more than just a gathering place. It was a place where immigrants came to write letters home, receive mail, and take care of business matters. Countrymen who had been in New York longer probably assisted the new arrivals.

These ink bottles revealed a side of Five Points that writers such as Dickens had not seen. Helping one another was an important part of life in Five Points. Working women often shared childcare and other household jobs. Men came together in groups such as trade unions. In many ways, people found companionship and support.

Immigrants in Five Points

From 1820 to 1870, large numbers of immigrants entered the United States. Five Points became home to several different immigrant groups.

In the first few decades of the nineteenth century, many Germans arrived. Among them were men who made and sold clothing. By the 1840s, Baxter Street had become New York City's first **garment** district. Retail and secondhand clothing stores, as well as the shops of tailors and shoemakers, lined the street. The tailors are gone, but their tools remain. Behind one of the shops, archaeologists uncovered a stone-lined privy full of pins, needles, thimbles, and cloth.

Irish immigrants prepare to leave Ireland for America.

By 1890, an Italian colony flourished in New York City.

Between 1845 and 1849, thousands of Irish people came to America to escape the Great Potato **Famine**. Many found their way to Five Points. From a material standpoint, their lives in Five Points were better than the lives they had left in Ireland. Here they had jobs. The men worked in construction, carpentry, masonry, and printing. The women worked in dressmaking, housekeeping, and hat making. Many of the children worked, too. Together, family members earned enough money to buy modest comforts. They ate meat almost every day. They bought items that were in fashion. The artifacts found behind the tenement at 474 Pearl Street include cologne [kuh·**lohn**] bottles, medicine bottles, a piece of an umbrella, a collar **stay,** and a fancy buckle.

In the 1880s, Italian immigrants began moving into Five Points. Some of these immigrants took over the clothing businesses when the German shopkeepers moved uptown. There were also some organ grinders among these new immigrants. In fact, archaeologists found the bones of a monkey behind a building on Baxter Street. The monkey might have belonged to an organ grinder who lived in that building.

Immigrants continued to find their way to Five Points well into the twentieth century. During the **Great Depression** of the 1930s, the number of very poor people living there grew. But even then, many of the Five Point inhabitants held jobs and felt part of a vital community.

famine (fam·in)—severe shortage of food

stay—strip of plastic or metal used to stiffen a piece of clothing

Great Depression (di·**presh**·uhn)—period in history when many people lost their jobs, homes, and money

Summary

Through archaeology, we have learned more about everyday life in Five Points. The possessions and other items that have been unearthed paint a picture of people's lives. This picture contradicts the accounts of that time. From the outside, Five Points appeared to be a frightful slum. From the inside, it was a thriving working-class neighborhood. In overcrowded and less than desirable conditions, the people of Five Points worked hard and lived respectable lives.

Put Your Habits to Work in

Literature | **Social Studies** | **Science** | **Math**

Before I Read Habit:
Check it out!

Depending on your purposes for reading, some parts of the selection will be more important than others. Remember to look at the title, summary, heads, and any maps before you read a chapter in your social studies textbook. Then decide which parts will best help you read for the reading purpose you have in mind.

The photos will help me...

While I Read Habit:
Stop and ask, "If it doesn't make sense, what can I do?"

If what you're reading doesn't make sense, look for ways to correct that so you understand. If you meet unfamiliar words, try using root words, prefixes, and suffixes to help you figure them out. Use a dictionary if you need one. Think about other words you know, too.

homesteading

After I Read Habit:
Check to see what I remember.

When you're reading a social studies book, check to see what you remember. One way to do so is to use examples from the text to question yourself about what you've read. Then answer your own questions.

Do I remember . . . ?

 You may wish to use the **Put Your Habits to Work Sheet** (page 59 in your *Strategy Practice Book*) to practice these habits in your other reading.

Habits and Strategies

Use this chart to review the nine good habits and the strategies you have been using. If you want, review the strategies by looking back at the unit.

Before I Read

1. Check it out!
- Find the parts that best tell what the selection is about. (Unit 1)
- Decide what the internal organization of the selection is. (Unit 5)
- Decide which parts will best help me read for the reading purpose I have in mind. (Unit 9)

2. Think about what I know about the subject.
- Identify the genre and decide what I know about this genre. (Unit 3)
- Preview the selection to see how these characters compare with characters in other stories I've read. (Unit 6)
- Look at graphic aids, photos, and their captions to decide what I know about the subject. (Unit 8)

3. Decide what I need to know.
- Use the title, heads, introduction, summary, and graphics to decide what the author wants me to understand. (Unit 2)
- Use graphic aids to ask purpose-setting questions. (Unit 4)
- Choose the features that best help me ask purpose-setting questions. (Unit 7)

While I Read

4. Stop and ask, "How does it connect to what I know?"
- Jot down a note about what the author is telling me and try to connect it to what I know. (Unit 2)
- Try to picture myself in a character's place. (Unit 6)
- Decide whether I agree with what I am reading. (Unit 8)

5. Stop and ask, "Does it make sense?"
- Jot down personal questions as I read. (Unit 1)
- Decide whether what I've read fits with what I know about the characters. (Unit 3)
- Identify the causes of events. (Unit 5)

6. Stop and ask, "If it doesn't make sense, what can I do?"
- Scan to find clarifying information. (Unit 4)
- Use word parts to help me understand words. (Unit 9)
- Select the best strategy (context clues, word parts, dictionary) to help me understand words. (Unit 7)

After I Read

7. React to what I've read.
- Decide whether the key points make sense and where I can go to check the author's facts. (Unit 2)
- Decide whether a different set of circumstances would have caused a different conclusion. (Unit 5)
- Decide whether the author was objective or biased. Give reasons why I think so. (Unit 8)

8. Check to see what I remember.
- Decide why I made certain inferences about characters and events. (Unit 3)
- Decide which features I should use to question myself about what I've read. (Unit 7)
- Use examples or explanations from the text to question myself about what I've read. (Unit 9)

9. Use what I've read.
- Decide how many of my personal questions were answered as I read. (Unit 1)
- Decide what I want to know more about. (Unit 4)
- Decide how I can apply what I read to a different situation. (Unit 6)